Cannabinoid Analysis in Physiological Fluids

Cannabinoid Analysis in Physiological Fluids

Joe A. Vinson, EDITOR

University of Scranton

Based on a symposium

sponsored by the Division

of Analytical Chemistry at the

173rd Meeting of the

American Chemical Society,

New Orleans, Louisiana,

March 20–25, 1977.

ACS SYMPOSIUM SERIES **98**

AMERICAN CHEMICAL SOCIETY

WASHINGTON, D. C.   1979

Library of Congress CIP Data

Cannabinoid analysis in physiological fluids.
  (ACS symposium series; 98 ISSN 0097-6156)

  Includes bibliographies and index.

  1. Tetrahydrocannabinol—Analysis—Congresses. 2.
Tetrahydrocannabinol—Metabolism—Congresses. 3.
Chemistry, Pharmaceutical—Congresses.
  I. Vinson, Joe A. II. American Chemical Society.
Division of Analytical Chemistry. III. Series: American
Chemical Society. ACS symposium series; 98.

RS431.T44C36   615'.323'962   79-10934
ISBN 0-8412-0488-8   ASCMC 8   98 1–242 1979

ACS Symposium Series

Robert F. Gould, *Editor*

FOREWORD

The ACS SYMPOSIUM SERIES was founded in 1974 to provide a medium for publishing symposia quickly in book form. The format of the Series parallels that of the continuing ADVANCES IN CHEMISTRY SERIES except that in order to save time the papers are not typeset but are reproduced as they are submitted by the authors in camera-ready form. Papers are reviewed under the supervision of the Editors with the assistance of the Series Advisory Board and are selected to maintain the integrity of the symposia; however, verbatim reproductions of previously published papers are not accepted. Both reviews and reports of research are acceptable since symposia may embrace both types of presentation.

CONTENTS

PREFACE

The preparations of *Cannabis sativa L.*, including marijuana and hash-ish, represent the most widely used group of illicit drugs in the world; they are consumed by an estimated 300 million people. A recent poll by the National Institute of Drug Abuse indicated that 53% of the population in the U.S. between the ages of 18 and 25 have tried marijuana and that the percentage is increasing.

In the last 15 years since Mechoulam isolated and identified the active ingredient in marijuana, tetrahydrocannabinol, scientific research has intensified, especially in the pharmacological area. The analytical chemistry of marijuana has progressed from the analysis of tetrahydro-cannabinol and other cannabinoids in plant material to the much more difficult problem of quantitation of tetrahydrocannabinol and its metabo-lites in physiological fluids. Recent advances in physiological fluid analy-sis were discussed in a symposium at the 173rd ACS National Meeting in New Orleans. This book offers representative papers from the different analytical methods presented at that meeting from worldwide experts in the field. Following an introductory paper, analytical methodologies using gas chromatography, mass spectroscopy, radioimmunoassay, high-pressure liquid chromatography, and thin-layer chromatography are presented.

It is a pleasure to express my gratitude to the participants in the symposium for their interest and enthusiasm as well as to their spirited discussions following presentation of the papers. To the authors of papers in this volume, a heartfelt thanks for their generous contribution of time and effort. The patience of my secretary, Debbie Camp, and the proofreading ability of my wife, Yvette, are also gratefully acknowledged.

University of Scranton   JOE A. VINSON
Scranton, PA 18510
January 2, 1979

A Survey of Metabolic Transformations of
Δ^1-Tetrahydrocannabinol

SUMNER BURSTEIN

Worcester Foundation for Experimental Biology, Shrewsbury, MA 01545

Comprehensive reviews of the metabolism of Δ^1-tetrahydrocannabinol (Δ^1-THC) are available (1,2) so that this paper will be limited to an overview of the subject with a somewhat greater emphasis on recent developments.

It is less than eight years since the first reports on this subject have appeared. At that time, four groups almost simultaneously published findings on both Δ^1 and Δ^6-THC, Nilsson et al. (3), Wall et al. (4), Foltz et al. (5) and Burstein et al. (6). All four laboratories independently showed that the 7 position was hydroxylated in both Δ^1 and Δ^6-THC (Figure 1). This has since been shown to be the major initial point of metabolism in virtually every system tested thus far.

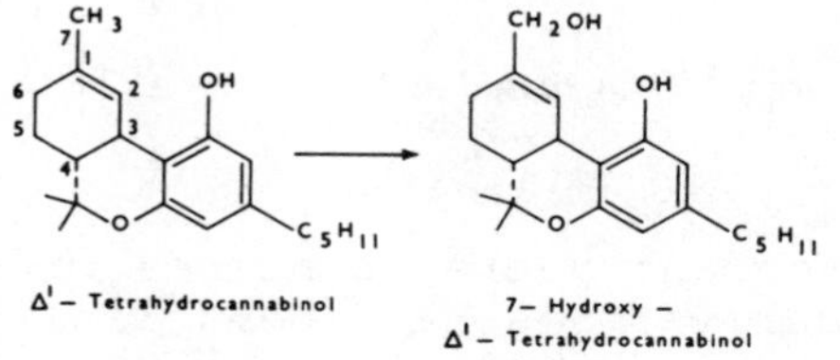

Δ^1 – Tetrahydrocannabinol   7– Hydroxy – Δ^1 – Tetrahydrocannabinol

Annals of the New York
Academy of Sciences

Figure 1.   Oxidation of Δ^1-THC (7)

0-8412-0488-8/79/47-098-001$05.00/0

The characteristics of this reaction were studied by Burstein and Kupfer (7) who showed that it followed the pattern of a typical mixed-function oxidase system. They showed that all the metabolizing activity occurred in the microsomal fraction and that oxygen and NADPH were required. Other agents such as SKF-525A (β-diethylaminoethyldiphenylpropyl acetate), Burstein and Kupfer (8), and DDT, Kupfer et al. (9), were reported to inhibit this hydroxylation process.

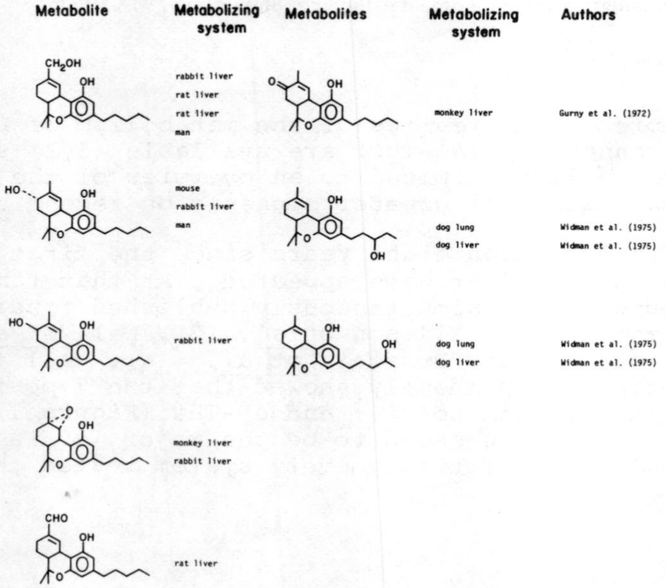

Figure 2.   Oxygenated metabolites of Δ¹-THC

In the subsequent years, a number of other monohydroxy-Δ¹-THC derivatives have been isolated from various metabolizing systems (Figure 2). These have been of two types: hydroxyls allylic to the Δ¹-double bond and sidechain hydroxyls. No evidence for aromatic hydroxylation has thus far been reported, although these positions are chemically reactive and there is biochemical evidence for C-C glucuronide formation at the 4'-position of Δ⁶-THC. Possibly such catechol type metabolites of Δ¹-THC are unstable and may be lost during the extraction and isolation procedures.

Another expected monohydroxy-Δ^1-THC which has thus
far remained undiscovered is 3-OH-Δ^1-THC. This position is both allylic and benzylic and would therefore
be expected to be highly susceptible to attack. The
possibility exists that this product is, in fact, formed
but may readily dissociate leading to a $\Delta^{1,3}$-diene
which could serve as a precursor to other more stable
metabolites such as cannabinol (CBN). This point will
be discussed further in connection with certain observed
transformations in a later section of this paper.

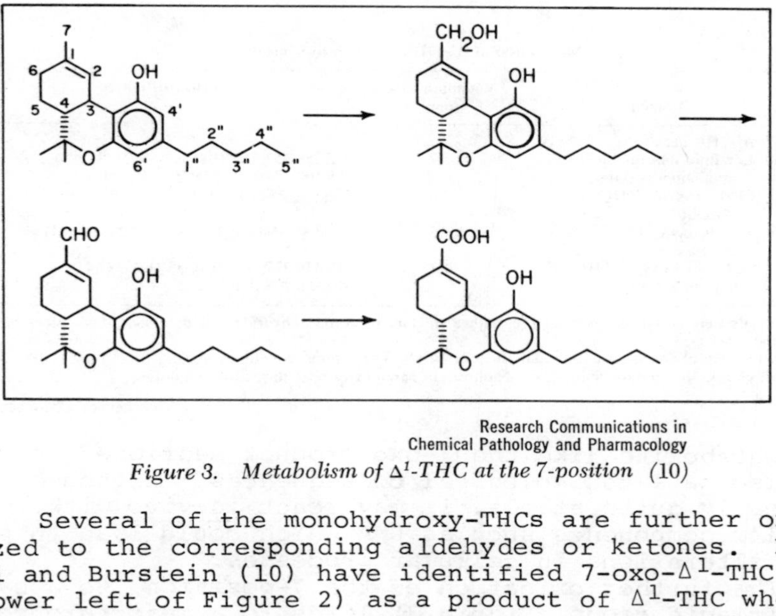

Research Communications in
Chemical Pathology and Pharmacology
Figure 3.   Metabolism of Δ^1-THC at the 7-position   (10)

Several of the monohydroxy-THCs are further oxidized to the corresponding aldehydes or ketones. Ben-
Zvi and Burstein (10) have identified 7-oxo-Δ^1-THC
(lower left of Figure 2) as a product of Δ^1-THC when
incubated with rat liver microsomes. Although it has
not been demonstrated, it seems certain that 7-OH-Δ^1-
THC is the precursor for this transformation (Figure
3). The levels of this aldehyde in human tissues are
unknown at this time, however, it is of interest to
speculate on the possible toxicological effects of such
a substance particularly in a chronic exposure situation. The α,β-unsaturated aldehydes such as crotonalde-
hyde are highly toxic and have been implicated in car-
cinogenesis. While 7-oxo-Δ^1-THC shows no acute effects,
long term exposure to this unsaturated aldehyde may
produce undesirable reactions.

Gurny et al. (11) have isolated 6-keto-Δ^1-THC from
the incubation of monkey liver with Δ^1-THC. As with
the aldehyde above, it seems likely that the corresponding hydroxy-THC is the precursor of this metabolite.

The compound 6α-OH-Δ^1-THC has been found by Wall (12) in human plasma so that it would not be surprising if there are detectable levels of the ketone as well.

A monooxygenated metabolite which arises by a different process is the $1\alpha,2\alpha$-epoxide (Figure 2). This substance was first reported by Gurny et al. (11) as a monkey liver product from Δ^1-THC; it has since been isolated by Ben-Zvi and Burstein (12) who used rabbit liver microsomes (Table 1).

Table 1

Metabolism of Δ^1-THC by rabbit liver microsomes (12)

T.l.c. zone	Rf	Assignment*	Retention time (min)	Principal ions† (M/e)
1	0·67	Δ^1-THC acetate		
2	0·40	1,2α-Epoxyhexahydro-cannabinol acetate	5·7	372(25), 357(25), 330(50), 315(75), 312(45) 298(100), 288(55), 274(75), 231(8·8)
		6α-Hydroxy-Δ^1-THC diacetate	7·0	372(3·4), 354(100), 339(21), 312(82), 297(65) 295(18)
3	0·30	7-Hydroxy-Δ^1-THC diacetate	7·5	372(3·8), 354(43), 312(100), 297(28), 259(31)
4	0·13	6α,7-Dihydroxy-Δ^1-THC triacetate	11·3	412(34), 397(5), 370(9), 355(12), 337(47) 310(46), 295(100)

* All materials were acetylated prior to t.l.c. with a mixture of acetic anhydride and pyridine. T.l.c. system: Silica gel G, hexane ether (7:3).
† The spectra were obtained on a Finnegan 1015 at 70 eV. The column conditions were: 2 ft, 2″, OV-1; 180 240 (8″/min); carrier gas, He; injector temp., 255°. Numbers in parentheses refer to relative intensities.

Biochemical Pharmacology

This metabolite like the 7-oxo product mentioned above may also have toxicological consequences. Although chemically quite stable, it may react in vivo with cellular components such as DNA which could lead to profound alterations in cellular processes.

The further oxidation of the 7-position, to a carboxylic acid group (Figure 3) leads to a major group of metabolic end products. The first substances identified in this series were side-chain hydroxylations. The 1"-and 2"-hydroxy derivatives which were reported by Burstein et al. (13) and shown in Figure 4. These were found in rabbit urine and appeared to be present as base-sensitive conjugates.

The parent Δ^1-THC-7-oic acid (lower left of Figure 4) has since been found in the monkey by Wall and Brine (14) and in the mouse, Harvey and Paton (15). The latter authors have also reported the 3"-hydroxy derivative and the 2",6-dihydroxy derivative as metabolites in the mouse (16). A series of acids in which the carboxyl group is in the side-chain have been isolated by Martin et al. (17). The structures were established by mass spectral analysis and by conversion to the corresponding alcohols which had been synthesized. The metabolites were shown to be 5"-nor-Δ^1-THC-4"-oic acid, 4",5"-bisnor-Δ^1-THC-3"-oic acid, and 3",4",5"-trisnor-Δ^1-THC-2"-oic acid; the second substance was a major product in the guinea pig. A fourth metabolite in which the side-chain was reduced to a single carboxyl group was tentatively identified; this substance is analogous to the CBN derivative which was tentatively reported by us (18,19). Nordquist et al. (20) identified a bisnor-dicarboxylic acid metabolite from the rabbit in which the side-chain is reduced to three carbon atoms (Figure 4). All of these acids and hydroxyacids probably represent detoxification products of Δ^1-THC since they are a major fraction of the excreted metabolites.

Polyhydroxy derivatives of Δ^1-THC have also been isolated by several groups (Figure 4). The positions involved are the same as those found for the monohydroxy-THCs and for the hydroxy-acids suggesting that these all arise by similar pathways.

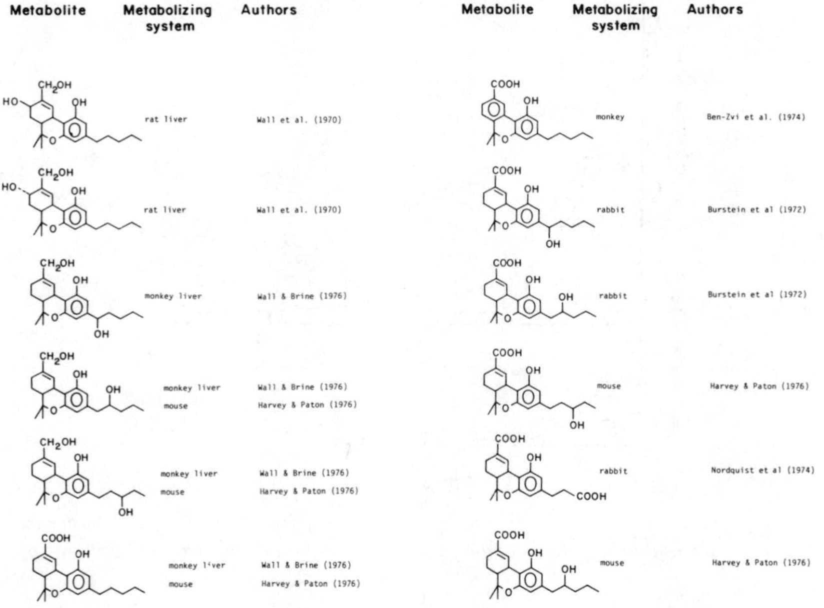

Metabolite	Metabolizing system	Authors	Metabolite	Metabolizing system	Authors
	rat liver	Wall et al. (1970)		monkey	Ben-Zvi et al. (1974)
	rat liver	Wall et al. (1970)		rabbit	Burstein et al (1972)
	monkey liver	Wall & Brine (1976)		rabbit	Burstein et al (1972)
	monkey liver / mouse	Wall & Brine (1976) / Harvey & Paton (1976)		mouse	Harvey & Paton (1976)
	monkey liver / mouse	Wall & Brine (1976) / Harvey & Paton (1976)		rabbit	Nordquist et al (1974)
	monkey liver / mouse	Wall & Brine (1976) / Harvey & Paton (1976)		mouse	Harvey & Paton (1976)

Figure 4. Polyoxygenated metabolites of Δ^1-THC

For some time it has been suspected that Δ^1-THC may be transformed into CBN in vivo. Widman et al. (21) found a small amount of CBN in rat bile which

could not be explained as a contaminant of the Δ^1-THC
which was administered. McCallum et al. (22) have
given more convincing evidence by monitoring rat blood
at short time intervals post injection (Figure 5). An
interesting feature of their findings was the very
transient nature of the CBN in blood. It seems that
the pharmacokinetics of CBN may be somewhat different
than that of Δ^1-THC.

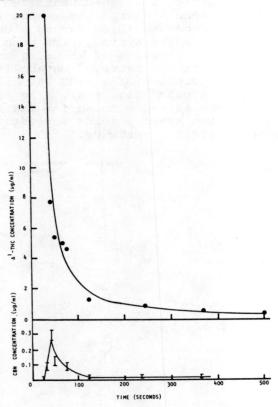

Raven Press

*Figure 5. Cannabinoid blood concentrations after iv administration of 1 mg of
Δ^1-THC to the rat (22)*

If CBN is formed in vivo, the appearance of oxygenated CBN metabolites as excretion products would be
expected and this has proven to be the cast. Quite independently, Ben-Zvi et al. (23) has identified CBN-7-
oic as a sizable fraction of the urinary monkey metabolites of Δ^1-THC. It is, of course, possible that
this metabolite could arise by a route not involving

CBN itself. As shown below in Figure 6, the aromatization process could occur after the oxidation of the
methyl group by a sequence such as outlined in the upper
part of the figure. All of the intermediates in this
proposed sequence have been shown to be metabolites of
Δ^1-THC lending support to this pathway.

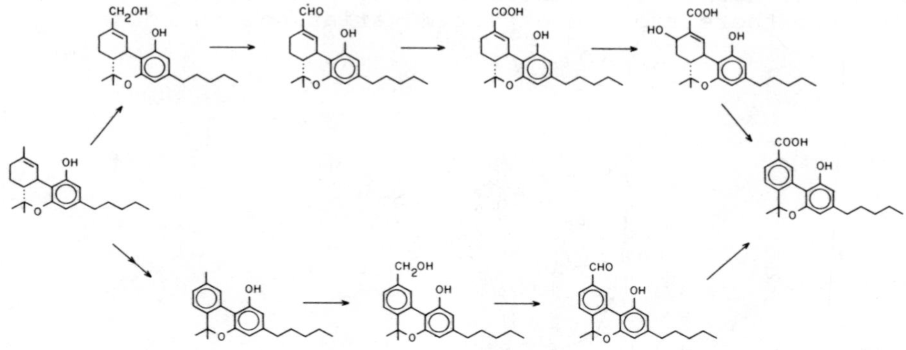

Raven Press

Figure 6.   Possible routes for the production of CBN-7-oic acid from Δ^1-THC (19)

The alternate route via CBN shown in the lower
part of Figure 6 is also supported by experimental
findings. CBN has been reported to be converted to 7-
OH-CBN by Widman et al. (24) and the further transformation to the acid was demonstrated by Burstein and
Varanelli (18).

The question of how Δ^1-THC could be transformed
to CBN was touched upon earlier in this paper. A
plausible explanation is that one of the three allylic
monohydroxy metabolites of Δ^1-THC undergoes a loss of
water to give the corresponding diene; this in turn
could be readily oxidized to the aromatic system (25).

In view of the nature of this symposium, it is
appropriate to mention several other aspects of THC
metabolism as a background for subsequent papers. As
in the above discussion on transformation products, the
subjects of route of administration, species variation,
excretion patterns and plasma levels are covered in
depth in several monographs by Mechoulam (25), Braude
and Szara (26) and Nahas et al. (27). Therefore, only
a limited number of reports will be cited as examples
of the type of data which has appeared.

As can be readily seen from Figure 7, Lemberger
(28) has found the route of administration has a major

effect on plasma levels of Δ^1-THC. The intravenous
route gave the highest values, inhalation was lower and
the oral route gave the lowest. This seems reasonable
since the drug in the first instance is injected directly into the compartment where it is subsequently
being measured. The plasma levels of metabolites are
somewhat higher than those of THC as is shown in Figure
8; also there are the expected variations in subjects.

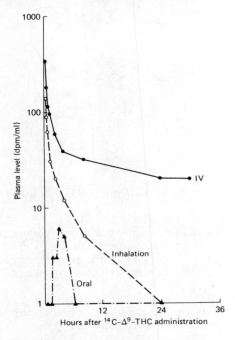

Springer-Verlag

*Figure 7. Plasma levels of unchanged ^{14}C-Δ^9-THC after oral or iv administration
and inhalation of ^{14}C-Δ^9-THC. Each curve represents a typical subject (28)*

Agurell (30) has observed species differences in
excretion patterns as is illustrated in Figure 9. The
rat resembles man in having a low proportion of metabolites in the urine; the rabbit, on the other hand,
disposes of most of the metabolites via the kidney.
These differences are also reflected in the rate of excretion; the rabbit being the most rapid.
The composition of the metabolite mixtures shows
a quantitative dependence on species. Table 2 compares the transformation of Δ^1-THC by rat and mouse
liver microsomes under similar conditions. While the
principal products were the same in both species, there

were substantial differences in the proportions of
each. Moreover, the mouse appeared to be more effective in metabolizing Δ¹-THC overall.

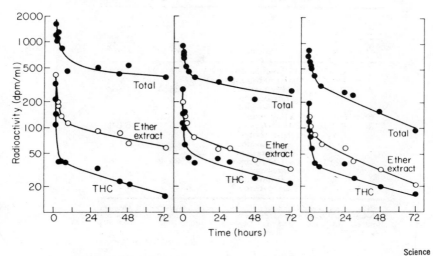

Science

*Figure 8. Plasma levels of Δ¹-THC, ether-extractable radioactivity, and total
radioactivity after iv injection of ¹⁴C-Δ¹-THC (5.6–7.9 μg/kg) in three human
subjects (29).*

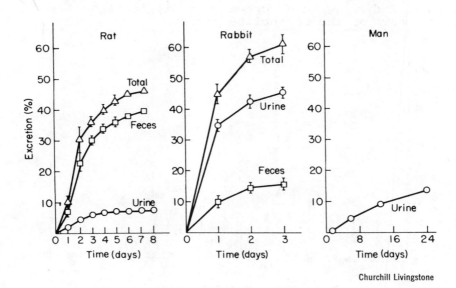

Churchill Livingstone

*Figure 9. Cumulative excretion of label after administration of ³H-Δ¹-THC in
rat, rabbit, and human urine and feces (30)*

Table 2

Metabolism of Δ¹-Tetrahydrocannabinol by
Liver Microsomes (31)

TLC Zone	R_f	Assignment[b]	Percent Recovered Products[a]	
			Mouse[c]	Rat[d]
1	0.67	Δ¹-Tetrahydro-cannabinol acetate	9.42	19.2
2	0.40	6α-Hydroxy-Δ¹-tetrahydro-cannabinol diacetate	26.3	10.0
3	0.30	7-Hydroxy-Δ¹-tetrahydro-cannabinol diacetate	34.1	53.3
4	0.13	6α,7-Dihydroxy-Δ¹-tetrahydro-cannabinol triacetate (?)	30.2	17.6

[a] Recoveries of added radioactivity were approximately 50%. [b] All materials were acetylated prior to TLC with a mixture of acetic anhydride and pyridine. [c] Adult male CD-1 mice (30–33 g). [d] Adult male Sprague–Dawley rats (190–230 g).

Journal of Pharmaceutical Sciences

In summary, it can be seen that Δ¹-THC is extensively transformed to a number of metabolites. Figure 10 shows a computer processed total ion chromatogram of the metabolites of Δ¹-THC from mouse liver. The main point in showing this chromatogram is to emphasize the complexity of the metabolite picture.

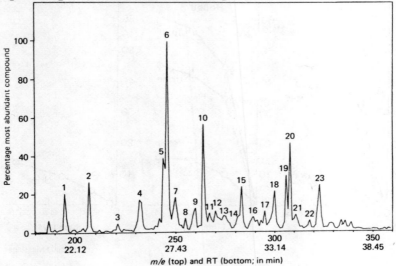

Springer-Verlag

Figure 10. The Δ¹-THC metabolite region of a gas chromatogram using only the ions above m/e = 210 (15)

This has been observed by others in the field using
different methods of analysis such as autoradiochroma-
tography. Despite the large number of products, there
seem to be a few pathways which account for most of the
metabolites thus far identified. These involve: (1)
oxidation allylic to the double bond, (2) side-chain
oxidation, and (3) aromatization.

   This situation presents a challenge to the analytical chemist, namely, which substance is the most appropriate for measurement. The answer would seem to depend on the origin of the sample as well as the inge-
nuity of the chemist in developing a sensitive, specific assay. In the case of forensic assays, legalistic
considerations will probably specify which substances
are to be measured. If the term "under the influence
of" is invoked, the levels of "active" metabolites will
also have to be measured before judgment can be passed.

REFERENCES

(1)   Burstein, S., in "Marijuana, Chemistry, Pharma-
       cology, Metabolism and Clinical Effects", Ed.
       R. Mechoulam, Academic Press, New York,   1973.
(2)   Mechoulam, R., McCallum, N. K., and Burstein, S.,
       Chem. Revs. 76, 75   (1976).
(3)   Nilsson, I. M., Agurell, S., Nilsson, J. L. G.,
       Ohlsson, A., and Wahlquist, M., *Science 168*, 1228
       (1970).
(4)   Wall, M. W., Brine, D. R., Brine, G. A., Pitt,
       C. G., Freudenthal, R. I., and Christensen, H. D.,
       J. Amer. Chem. Soc. 92, 3466   (1970).
(5)   Foltz, R. L., Fentiman, A. F., Jr., Leighty, E. G.,
       Walter, J. L., Drewes, H. R., Schwartz, W. E.,
       Page, T. F., Jr. and Truitty, E. B., Jr., *Science
       168*, 844   (1970).
(6)   Burstein, S., Menezes, F., Williamson, E., and
       Mechoulam, R., *Nature (London) 225*, 88   (1970).
(7)   Burstein, S., and Kupfer, D., *Ann. N. Y. Acad.
       Sci. 191*, 61   (1971).
(8)   Burstein, S., and Kupfer, D., *Chem.-Biol. Inter-
       actions 3*, 316   (1971).
(9)   Kupfer, D., Levin, E., and Burstein, S., *Chem.-
       Biol. Interact. 6*, 59   (1973).
(10)   Ben-Zvi, Z., and Burstein, S., *Res. Comm. Chem.
       Pathol. Pharmacol. 8*, 223   (1974).
(11)   Gurny, O., Maynard, D. E., Pitcher, R. G., and
       Kierstead, R. W., *J. Amer. Chem. Soc. 95*, 7978
       (1972).
(12)   Ben-Zvi, Z., and Burstein, S., *Biochem. Pharmacol.
       24*, 1130   (1975).

(13) Burstein, S., Rosenfeld, J., and Wittstruck, T.,
      Science 176, 422   (1972).
(14) Wall, M. E., and Brine, D. R., in "Marijuana:
      Chemistry, Biochemistry and Cellular Effects",
      Ed. G. Nahas, Springer-Verlag, New York, 1976,Ch. 5.
(15) Harvey, D. J., and Paton, W. D. M., in "Mari-
      juana: Chemistry, Biochemistry and Cellular
      Effects", Ed. G. Nahas, Springer-Verlag, New York,
      1976, Ch. 9.
(16) Harvey, D. J., and Paton, W. D. M., *Res. Comm.
      Chem. Pathol. and Pharmacol. 13*, 585   (1976).
(17) Martin, B. R., Harvey, D. J., and Paton, W. D. M.,
      J. Pharm. and Pharmacol. 28, 773   (1976).
(18) Burstein, S., and Varanelli, C., *Res. Comm. Chem.
      Pathol. Pharmacol. 11*, 343   (1975).
(19) Ben-Zvi, Z., Bergen, J. R., Burstein, S., Sehgal,
      P. K., and Varanelli, C., in "The Pharmacology
      of Marijuana", Eds. M. C. Braude and S. Szara,
      Raven Press, New York, 1976, p. 63.
(20) Nordquist, M., Agurell, S., and Binder, M., *J.
      Pharm. Pharmacol. 26*, 471   (1974).
(21) Widman, M., Nordquist, M., Agurell, S., Lindgren,
      J.-E., and Sandberg, F., *Biochem. Pharmacol. 23*,
      1163 (1974).
(22) McCallum, N. K., Yagen, B., Levy, S., and Mechou-
      lam, R., in "Pharmacology of Marijuana", Eds.
      M. C. Braude and S. Szara, Raven Press, New York,
      1976, p. 43.
(23) Ben-Zvi, Z., Bergen, J. R., and Burstein, S.,
      Res. Comm. Chem. Pathol. Pharmacol. 9, 201   (1974).
(24) Widman, M., Nilsson, I. M., Nilsson, J. R. G.,
      Agurell, S., and Leander, K., *Life Sci. 10*, 157
      (1971).
(25) Mechoulam, R., Ed., "Marijuana: Chemistry, Phar-
      macology, Metabolism and Clinical Effects",
      Academic Press, New York 1973.
(26) Braude, M. C., and Szara, S., Eds., "Pharmacology
      of Marijuana", Raven Press, New York, 1976.
(27) Nahas, G., Ed., "Marijuana: Chemistry, Biochemis-
      try and Cellular Effects", Springer-Verlag, New
      York, 1976.
(28) Lemberger, L., in "Marijuana: Chemistry, Bio-
      chemistry and Cellular Effects", Ed. G. Nahas,
      Springer-Verlag, New York, 1976, Ch.14.
(29) Lemberger, L., Silberstein, S. D., Axelrod, J.,
      and Kopin, I. J., *Science 170*, 1320   (1970).
(30) Agurell, S., Nilsson, A., and Sandberg, F., in
      "Botany and Chemistry of Cannabis", Joyce and Curry,
      Eds., Churchill Livingstone, London, 1970, p. 184.
(31) Ben-Zvi, Z., Burstein, S., and Zikopoulos, J.,
      J. Pharm. Sci. 63, 1173   (1974).

RECEIVED December 12, 1978.

GLC and HPLC Analyses of Cannabinoids in Biological Fluids and Applications

E. R. GARRETT[1a], A. J. GOUYETTE[1b], and C. A. HUNT[1c]

College of Pharmacy, University of Florida, Gainesville, FL 32610

Pharmacological and metabolic studies on cannabinoids (Fig. 1) have suffered from a lack of knowledge of their physico-chemical properties and the insensitivity of assays of Δ^9-tetrahydrocannabinol $\underline{1}$, and its metabolites in biological fluids. Unambiguous, sensitive, specific and accurate quantification is required for forensic toxicology and pharmacokinetic studies which can be correlated with the time course of the psychoactive effects (2).

The determination (3) of physical and chemical properties such as solubility, stability, pKa, glass-binding and protein-binding of Δ^9-tetrahydrocannabinol $\underline{1}$ and correlated congeners were only possible after the development of new high pressure liquid chromatography (HPLC) techniques and the modification of gas liquid chromatography (GLC) technologies.

Clinical investigations of Δ^9-tetrahydrocannabinol (4,5) and 11-hydroxy-Δ^9-tetrahydrocannabinol (6) have relied upon analysis by radioactive labeling. However, the study of distribution, metabolism and excretion of the drug and its metabolites under chronic or "street" conditions demands nonradioactive analytical procedures. When plasma suspensions of ^{14}C-Δ^9-tetrahydrocannabinol were administered intravenously to three dogs at doses of 0.1 - 2.0 mg/kg and plasma levels of $\underline{1}$ were followed for up to 7000 minutes, no significant differences were seen in $\underline{1}$ plasma levels as determined by liquid scintillation and electron capture detection (GLC) after HPLC collection.

0-8412-0488-8/79/47-098-013$06.25/0

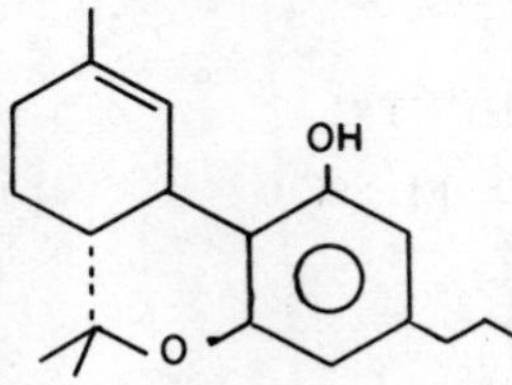

Δ^9 - tetrahydrocannabinol <u>1</u>

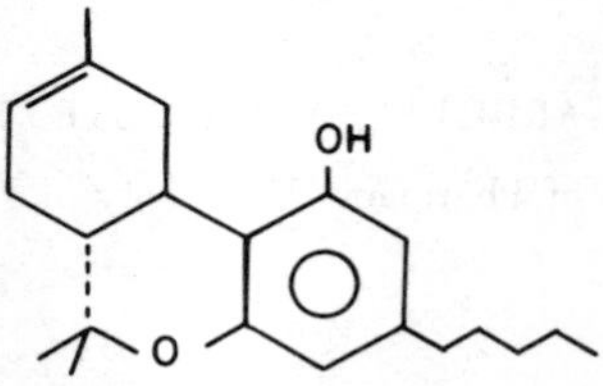

Δ^8 - tetrahydrocannabinol <u>2</u>

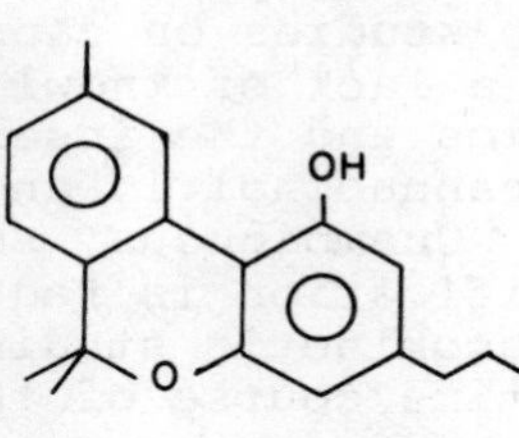

Cannabinol <u>12</u>

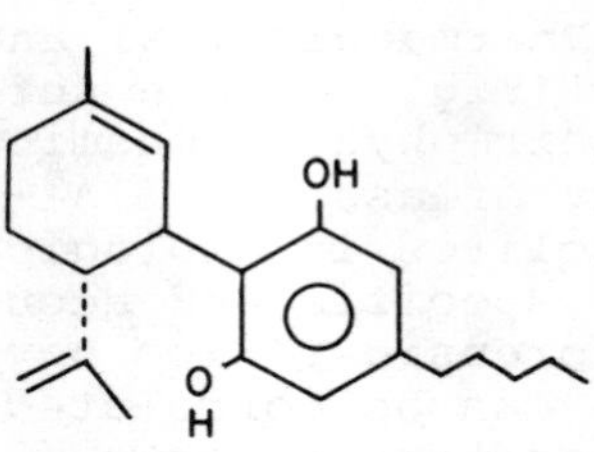

Cannabidiol <u>10</u>

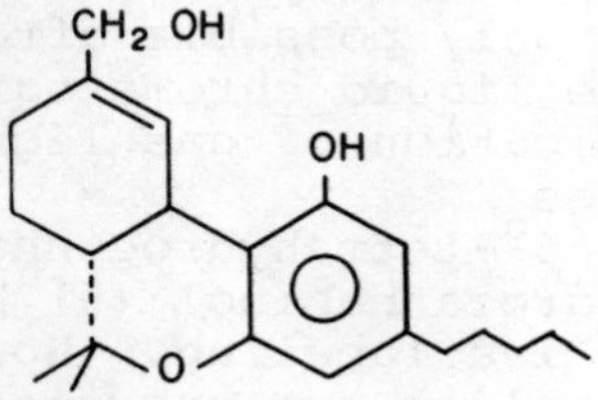

11 - hydroxy -
Δ^9 - tetrahydrocannabinol

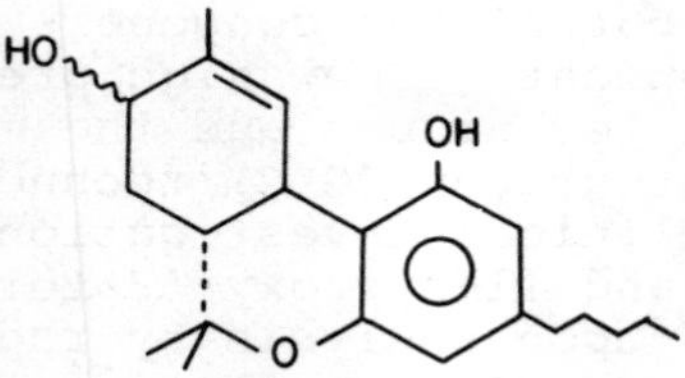

8 α or 8 β - hydroxy -
Δ^9 - tetrahydrocannabinol

Figure 1.   Structural formulas of some cannabinoids

PHYSICOCHEMICAL PROPERTIES OF
Δ^9-TETRAHYDROCANNABINOL

Solubility

Δ^9-tetrahydrocannabinol is a liquid and is highly
insoluble in water (8-10). This can be a critical factor in its bioavailability, pharmacokinetics and pharmacological action. Large differences in the bioavailability of tetrahydrocannabinol from various solutions
and administrative routes have been reported (9,10).
Evidence has been presented (8) that tetrahydrocannabinol's solubility may be exceeded in plasma, resulting
in its possible precipitation and fortuitous localized
accumulation in body organs.
The solubilities of Δ^9-tetrahydrocannabinol were
determined (7) by two methods: 1) Beer's law plots were
obtained by plotting the absorbance at one wavelength
(225 nm) versus the amount of tetrahydrocannabinol
added. The solubility of tetrahydrocannabinol was determined as that concentration at which deviation from
Beer's law was observed; 2) A modification of the procedure of Saad and Higuchi (11) for determining solubility by using a particle-size counter was also used;
1 formed micelles when its solubility was exceeded and
the appearance of these micelles was monitored by the
counter.
The solubility of 1 increased as a linear function
of ethanol concentration (at constant ionic strength)
and decreased with the square root of the ionic
strength (at constant ethanol concentration). "Salting-
out" coefficients were determined. The solubility of
1 in 0.15 M NaCl was 0.77 mg/liter at 23° and extrapo-
lation estimated a solubility of 2.8 mg/liter in pure
water.
The particle-size counting procedure overestimated
the true solubility since there is a limit below which
particle size cannot be counted. The mean solubility
estimate was 1.05 mg/liter by this method in 0.9% NaCl
(0.154 $\underline{M}$), in good agreement with the spectrophotometric method.

Spectrophotometric Determination of the pK'_a(7)

The pK'_a of tetrahydrocannabinol was calculated by
employing the modified form of the Henderson-Hasselbach
equation (12):

$$\log \{ (\varepsilon_b - \varepsilon) \ / \ (\varepsilon - \varepsilon_a) \}_\lambda = pH - pK'_a$$

where ε_a(5,850) and ε_b(12,226) are the molar absorbtivities of the unionized and completely ionized drug measured at the given wavelength λ (240 nm), respectively, and ε is the apparent molar absorptivity of a solution measured at a particular pH. The absorptivities of the ionized and unionized species were estimated using 0.5 N HCl and 0.5 N NaOH. The pK'$_a$ was 10.56 ± 0.16 (σ) in accordance with Equation 1 (Fig. 2).

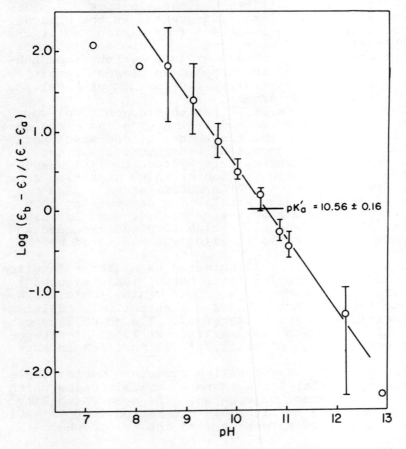

Journal of Pharmaceutical Sciences

Figure 2.   Spectrophotometric determination of the pK'$_a$ of Δ^9-THC in accordance with log $\{(\epsilon_b - \epsilon)/(\epsilon - \epsilon_a)\} = pH - pK'_a$, where ϵ_a and ϵ_b are the molar absorptivities of the unionized and completely ionized drug at 240 nm, respectively, and ϵ is the apparent molar absorptivity at the stated pH value (7).

This pK'$_a$ is higher than would be anticipated for ortho- and meta- substituted phenols since the o methoxyphenol has a pK'$_a$ of 9.98, m-methoxyphenol a pK'$_a$ of 9.65 and resorcinol a pK'$_a$ of 9.81 (13). A molecular model of the drug shows that the free rotation of the phenolic hydrogen is hindered by the Δ^9-hydrogen and can explain Δ^9-tetrahydrocannabinol's higher pK'$_a$. Of course, if solvated dimers, trimers, etc., exist with hydrophobic bonding, the observed pK'$_a$ could be a hybrid pK'$_a$ for a solution of such polymers.

Glassbinding

The rate and extent of tetrahydrocannabinol (in aqueous solution) binding to glass depend on the surface area of the glass, the pretreatment of the glass, and the concentration of the drug. About 20 and 40%, respectively, of tetrahydrocannabinol bind in 50 ml volumetric flasks at concentrations of 0.1 and 0.05 μg/ml. At high drug concentrations (0.5 - 1.0 μg/ml) and after full equilibration, less than 7% of the amount in an aqueous solution was bound to glass from various flasks and test tubes.

Preconditioning glass with strong alkali or acid did not decrease the extent of binding. New, unused glassware bound the drug to a similar extent. Treatment of the flasks with a water soluble silicone concentrate increased the extent of binding. However, vigorous shaking immediately prior to sampling reduced the degree of binding, but no more than 50% in any case.

Trimethysilyl treatment of glassware significantly reduced binding. However, at room temperature the bound fraction of a 0.1 μg/ml solution increased to the pretreatment level after 300 minutes.

Polycarbonate, polypropylene, Teflon[R], and stainless steel containers showed more extensive binding than glass (Fig. 3). Significant retention on glass pipets was observed. Of great importance in the light of normal handling of samples of biological fluids is the fact that 70 - 97% of the drug in the vials was lost to the rubber stopper after one hour of shaking of the stoppered vials.

Tetrahydrocannabinol in whole blood or plasma also binds to glass. However, since tetrahydrocannabinol protein binding is very large, glass binding is significantly reduced. The binding of drug from plasma to the silyl-treated glassware was negligible.

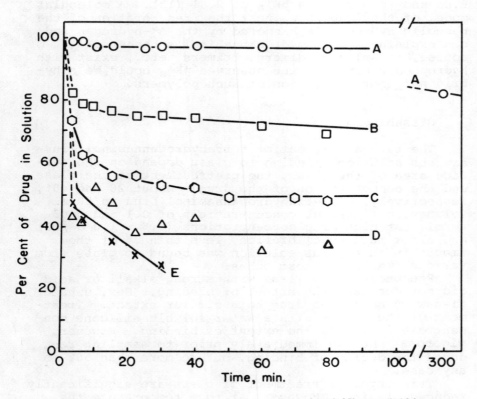

*Figure 3. Glass binding of Δ^9-THC showing the percent of drug added that re-
mained in solution at various times for: (A) TMS-treated 50-mL volumetric flasks
from an aqueous drug concentration of 0.1 μg/mL; (B) an aqueous drug concentration of 0.1 μg/mL in untreated 50-mL volumetric flasks; (C) an aqueous drug
concentration of 0.1 μg/mL in water-soluble silicone concentrate-treated 50-mL
volumetric flasks; (D) an aqueous drug concentration of 0.05 μg/mL in untreated
50-mL volumetric flasks; and (E) an aqueous drug concentration of 0.1 μg/mL in
a 20-mL stainless steel ultracentrifuge tube. Each point is the mean of four separate determinations (7).*

Protein-Binding

When tetrahydrocannabinol in isotonic phosphate
buffer was dialyzed against isotonic phosphate buffer,
50 - 100% of the drug was bound to the tubing used as
the membrane. All of the drug was bound below 0.05
µg/ml. Ultrafiltration was equally unsuccessful, since
only 0 - 5% of the drug in isotonic phosphate buffer
was recovered in the ultrafiltrate.

The only other known study on the binding of Δ^9-
tetrahydrocannabinol to plasma proteins was performed
with electrophoretic techniques on tritium-labeled
material and human plasma (14). The compound was 90 -
95% associated with lipoproteins.

Because of this extensive plasma protein binding,
a method of variable plasma concentrations was devised
(7) which took advantage of the competition between red
blood cells and plasma protein for the free drug in
plasma water. The red blood cell distribution coefficient, $D = (A_{RBC})/(A_p^u)$, was 12.5 for the dog red blood
cells where (A_{RBC}) is the concentration of drug in the
red blood cells and (A_p^u) is the concentration of unbound drug in plasma. The function of tetrahydrocannabinol bound to plasma protein was independent of
drug concentration. The fraction 0.972 of tetrahydrocannabinol in plasma was bound at normal protein concentrations. The developed procedure can be used
routinely to determine the protein binding of individual subjects. It permits more accurate estimates at
high degrees of protein binding which the normal errors
in classical methods would not allow.

SEPARATION AND ANALYSES

Purification of Cannabinoids by High Pressure
Liquid Chromatography (HPLC) (15,16)

The ^{14}C-Δ^9-tetrahydrocannabinol used as supplied by
NIDA was checked for purity on reverse and normal phase
HPLC and was contaminated by two compounds which were
not further analyzed. The quality of the water used in
the eluting solvent acetonitrile-water in reverse phase
(column: Bondapack C-18^R; eluent: 45% acetonitrile in
water at 2.5 ml/min) was an important factor in main-
taining the reproducibility of the percent radioactivity recovered for a given collection range. On
normal phase HPLC (column: µ-Porasil^R, eluent: 5%
tetrahydrofuran in n-hexane at 0.5 ml/min) Δ^8- and

Δ^9-tetrahydrocannabinol were quantitatively separated
with respective retention volumes of 6.37 and 6.62 ml
(the dead volume between the UV detector and the collection point was 0.46 ml as determined by the iodoform
test). Cannabidiol in the same system had a retention
volume of 6.06 ml.

The ethanolic stock solution of trans-cannabidiol
10, originally analyzed by gas liquid chromatography
(GLC) (column: 3% OV-17 on 100-120 mesh Gas Chrom Q,
1.8 m, 240) showed contamination with traces of hexahydrocannabinol 11, Δ^9-tetrahydrocannabinol 1 (12.2%),
cannabinol 12 (0.65%) and three unidentified compounds
(total 0.66%). This solution was purified on two
μ-Porasil^R column in series, using 5% tetrahydofuran in
n-hexane (0.5 ml/min), where the retention volume of
cannabinol 10. Δ^8-tetrahydrocannabinol 2, and Δ^9-
tetrahydrocannabinol 1, were 13.3, 14.0 and 14.6 ml
respectively (Fig. 4). GLC analysis of the cannabinol
collections showed greater than 99.5% purity with less
than 0.3% contamination by tetrahydrocannabinol and
negligible other peaks.

Another solvent system was also used to resolve
tetrahydrocannabinol, cannabinol and cannabidiol by the
normal phase HPLC (column: μ-Porasil^R; eluent; 20%
chloroform in heptane at 2.5 ml/min). However, the
chosen collection range would also collect cannabinol
and cannabidiol if 98% of the tetrahydrocannabinol were
to be collected. The retention volumes of cannabidiol
and cannabinol relative to 1 significantly diverged
with increasing percentages of increased percent of
chloroform in heptane to give better separation.

The monohydroxylated metabolites had large retention volumes (> 15 ml) on the normal phase column when
20% chloroform in heptane was the solvent and could be
completely separated from tetrahydrocannabinol on this
system. They were resolved from each other with a more
polar solvent, 80% chloroform in heptane.

Δ^9-Tetrahydrocannabinol and 11-hydroxy-Δ^9-tetra-
hydrocannabinol were quantitatively separable on the
reverse phase HPLC system at 47% (or less) acetonitrile
in water. The collection efficiencies in the chosen
ranges were 98% of the recoverable radioactivities of
^{3}H-11-hydroxy-Δ^9-tetrahydrocannabinol and ^{14}C-Δ^9-
tetrahydrocannabinol (Fig. 5). Δ^8- and Δ^9-Tetrahydro-
cannabinol were not readily resolvable in any of these
systems. However, the pooled fraction of 1 and 2 could
be resolved (Fig. 4) on the normal phase HPLC (5% tetrahydrofuran in n-hexane).

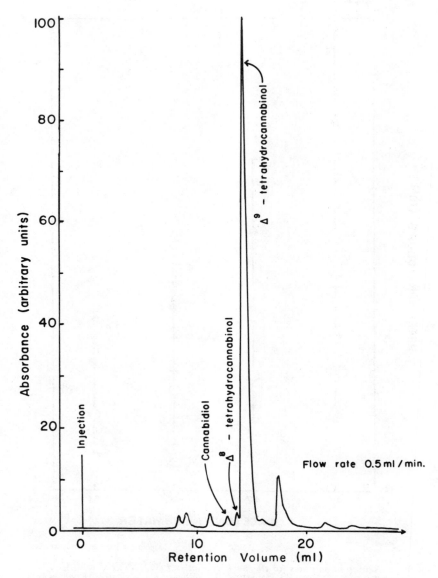

Figure 4.   Normal phase HPLC separation of cannabinoids (two μ-Porasil® columns in series) using 5% THF in n-hexane at a flow rate of 0.5 mL/min

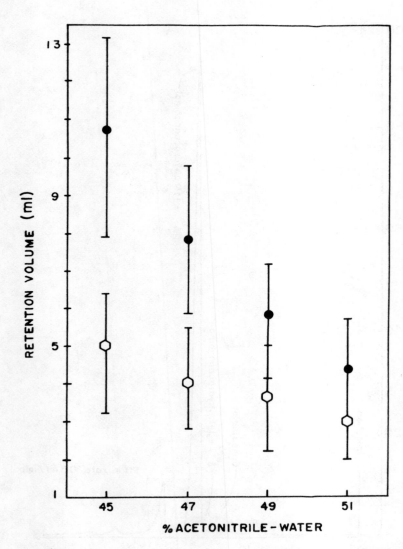

Figure 5.   Retention volumes for the peak amounts of (●), Δ⁹-THC and (◌), 11-hydroxy-Δ⁹-THC for reverse-phase HPLC vs. solvent composition.   Each point represents the mean peak retention volume for two determinations.   The vertical bars represent the ranges of retention volumes that contained approximately 98% of the area under the plot of recovered radioactivity vs. retention volume (15).

Cannabinol, Δ^8- and Δ^9-tetrahydrocannabinol had the same retention volumes of 0.05 ml on a μ-Porasil[R] column with 30% tetrahydrofuran in n-hexane and were separated from the acid degradation products with respective retention volumes of 9.5 and 11.0 ml. The collection fraction containing the tetrahydrocannabinol could be purified later using the 5% tetrahydrofuran-hexane solvent system.

Effect of HPLC Separation on GLC Analysis of Δ^9-Tetrahydrocannabinol in Plasma (15)

An equal amount of Δ^9-tetrahydrocannabinol and 11-hydroxy-Δ^9-tetrahydrocannabinol in 2 ml dog plasma (the pH was adjusted between 9.5 and 11.0 by addition of 0.1 N Na_2CO_3 prepared from water purified using a Bondapak C 18[R] column) was extracted in a silylated tube by heptane with 1.5% isoamyl alcohol. In this extract, the compounds were separated from a majority of extracted components by reverse phase HPLC. The reduction in potential contaminants from plasma observable on GLC was demonstrated by flame ionization GLC analysis (17,18) both before and after HPLC treatment (Fig. 6).

The normal phase HPLC (20% chloroform in heptane) could separate Δ^9-tetrahydrocannabinol from monohydroxylated metabolites and from 11-hydroxy-Δ^9-tetrahydrocannabinol. However, a minor overlap could be avoided by collecting the tetrahydrocannabinol 1 in a slightly narrower volume range. The prior heptane extraction of alkalinized plasma had separated these non-polar constituents from any acidic metabolite. This separation of plasma extracts and normal phase HPLC collection of volumes in the appropriate range resulted in a substantial reduction in GLC background from plasma components for derivatized tetrahydrocannabinol analyzed with electron capture (^{63}Ni) detection.

Plasma samples obtained from dogs, administered Δ^9-tetrahydrocannabinol solutions intraveneously, were analyzed by the electron capture GLC in accordance with the modified procedures described herein that included extraction, normal phase HPLC separation and derivatization except that no internal standard was added. These procedures would have included any cannabinol or cannabidiol in the HPLC collection volume range used. However, no peaks were seen at the retention times of cannabinol or cannabinol pentafluorobenzoate and no significant amounts of cannabinol or cannabidiol could be detected as metabolites of 1 in the dog. Thus

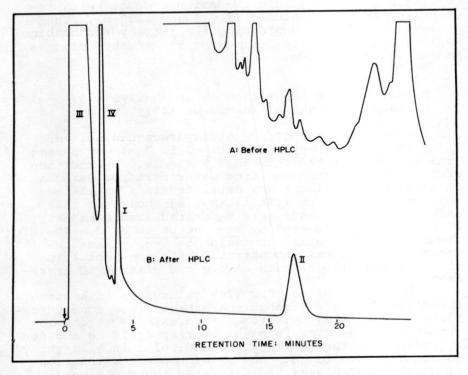

Journal of Pharmaceutical Sciences

Figure 6. GLC (FID) of an extract of 2 mL of plasma containing Δ^9-THC, Peak I (200 ng/mL), and 11-hydroxy-Δ^9-THC, Peak II (200 ng/mL), before (A) and after (B) reversed-phase HPLC separation of both cannabinoids over a range of predetermined collection volumes.

(A) A 1 mL aliquot of 18 μL of extract was injected into the gas chromatograph prior to HPLC. (B) A 10 mL aliquot of 18 μL of the extract was injected into the liquid chromatograph; the collected fraction was reconstituted in 10 μL of chloroform, and 1 μL was injected into the gas chromatograph. Peak III is the solvent; Peak IV is an unknown from plasma. For HPLC, the column was Corasil C_{18}; the eluent was 51% acetonitrile in water at 1.5 mL/min. For GLC, the column was 1.5 m (5 ft) $\times$ 2 mm, 1.9% OV-225 at 245°, with a nitrogen flow of 24 mL/min. An attenuation of 8×10^{-12} was used for both chromatograms. The initial baselines and injection times for both chromatograms are superimposed for comparison (15).

either compound, when purified should serve as an appropriate internal standard in pharmacokinetic studies. Since cannabinol has been reported as a minor metabolite (19,20), cannabidiol pentafluorobenzoate was chosen as the internal standard. It must be realized that cannabinol, now, is known to be a contaminant of degraded Δ^9-tetrahydrocannabinol (16,18).

The GLC methodology presented herein differed from prior studies (17) in that the short 30 cm column of 3% OV-225 was supplanted by a longer OV-17 packed column to be consistent with the data in the literature accumulated for the resolution of the cannbinols (23-25).

However, the efficiencies of the separation of these two types of columns (OV-17 and OV-225) were compared for a mixture and the HPLC purified products of the acid degradation (15) of 1 by flame ionization detection. The retention times for both columns are given in Table I and clearly show the superiority of OV-225 in peak separation of these particular compounds.

TABLE I

Comparison of Retention Times of a Mixture of HPLC-Purified Cannabinoids and Products of Acid Degradation of Different Columns* (From Reference 16)

Compounds	OV-225		OV-17	
	Retention time (min)	Ret. time relative to 4	Retention time (min)	Ret. time relative to 4
Δ^8-Tetrahydro-cannabinol 2	4.93	0.38	4.65	0.58
Δ^9-Tetrahydro-cannabinol 1	5.53	0.41	5.19	0.64
Cannabinol 12	8.45	0.64	6.43	0.80
9,10-Dihydro-9-hydroxyiso-cannabidiol 6	10.62	0.81	7.35	0.91
9-Hydroxy-hexahydro-cannabinol 4	13.14	1.00	8.07	1.00

*3% on Gas Chrom Q (100-120 mesh); column, length 1.8m, temperature 235°; detector and injector temperature, 260°; helium flow, 35 ml/min; hydrogen flow, 30 ml/min; air flow, 300 ml/min.

Journal of Pharmaceutical Sciences

APPLICATIONS

Stability of Tetrahydrocannabinol in Aqueous Solutions (16,18)

Previous studies (18) on the stability of Δ^9-tetrahydrocannabinol in acidic media below pH 4 monitored by GLC demonstrated an apparent biphasic semilogarithmic plot of undegraded 1 against time; either there was formed an intermediate which has the same retention time as 1 that also gave rise to the observed products or there was a relatively rapid equilibration of Δ^9-tetrahydrocannabinol 1 with another compound and slower further irreversible degradation of one or all of these compounds. (The studies were performed with ^{14}C-labeled and non-labeled 1). Since the possible reasons why this problem was not solved were that the specific activity or the concentration were too low, additional studies (16) at concentrations about 10 mg/l of HPLC purified 1 were carried out in 20% ethanolic solutions (0.1N HCl). The GLC (OV-17) analyses of the degraded products are summarized in Table 2. The retention times of the different compounds were the

TABLE 2

GLC^a Characterization of Acid Degradation^b of HPLC-Purified Δ^9-Tetrahydrocannabinol in 20% Ethanol in 0.1 N HCl (from reference 16)

Retention time (min)	Percent of Total Area^c	Compound
4.00	0.66	Cannabinol 10
4.90	1.49	Δ^8-Tetrahydrocannabinol 2
5.44	81.53	Δ^9-Tetrahydrocannabinol 1
6.66	9.62	Cannabinol 12
7.43	2.57	9,10-Dihydroxy-9-hydroxy-isocannabidiol 6
8.43	1.55	9-Hydroxyhexahydrocannabinol 4
9.18	2.16	6,12-Dihydro-6-hydroxy-cannabidiol 8

a OV-17 column 240°, injector 290°; detector 300°; helium, 35 ml/min; air, 300 ml/min; hydrogen, 30 ml/min.
b 100 ml 1.0 N HCl, 200 ml EtOH, 700 ml H_2O at 60° for 30 min.
c The total is not 100% since there are some minor unidentified peaks.

same as for purified authentic materials. The identification of cannabidiol 10 at retention time of 4.00 minutes and 6,12-dihydro-6-hydroxy-cannabidiol 8, at 9.18 minutes was done by GC-mass spectrometry. Equilibria could then be postulated among Δ^9-tetrahydrocannabinol 1, cannabidiol 10, 6,12-dihydro-6-hydroxycannabidiol 8 and possibly isocannabidiol 9 (Scheme I). This was challenged by subjecting HPLC purified cannabidiol 10 (with a Δ^9-tetrahydrocannabinol content less than 0.3%) to degradation under the same conditions and assaying the resultant products by GLC (Table 3). The appearance of 1, 6 and 8 was confirmatory.

Furthermore, a kinetic study of cannabidiol degradation using 4-androsten-3,17-dione as an internal standard showed a biphasic decline in semilogarithmic plotting against time (16). Concomitant with the initial decline is an appearance of Δ^9-tetrahydrocannabinol 1, undoubtly due to acid-catalyzed cyclization. The almost simultaneous appearance of 8 can be due to the reversible acid-catalyzed hydration of the exocyclic double bond of cannabidiol 10, or the acidic cleavage of the ether linkage of 1 in the equilibrium. The retarded appearance of 6 indicates that acid-catalyzed hydration of the endocyclic bond may preferentially be effected only when the intact ether linkage of 1 exists. The final equilibria must favor 4, 6 and Δ^8-tetrahydrocannabinol 2 where dehydration of 4 favors the Δ^8-configuration.

The formation of cannabinol in nitrogen purged acidic solutions was difficult to explain in the absence of oxidizing agents (18). The probable route is by a disproportionation of 1 to hexahydrocannabinol 11 and cannabinol 12. GLC analyses (16) of the contents of acid aqueous solutions of 1 (reacted under different conditions) gave significant areas under the peaks assignable to hexahydrocannabinol 11 and cannabinol. Both peaks were present together; both were absent when degradations were effected in HPLC purified water and when the glassware was previously silylated (Regisil[R]). The use of TLC purified 1 showed both products 11 and 12. Also, when the water used was pre-extracted with chloroform, for both untreated or aqueous-silicone (Siliclad[R]) coated glassware, both of these products were present in high evidence.

Thus it can be concluded that traces of chloroform in the reaction mixture and traces of silicic acid from TLC plates catalyze the formation of free radicals and lead to the disproportionation of 1 to 11 and 12 (Scheme II). The radical 13 is stabilized by the benzene ring and the allylic activation of the C-10 benzlic hydrogen.

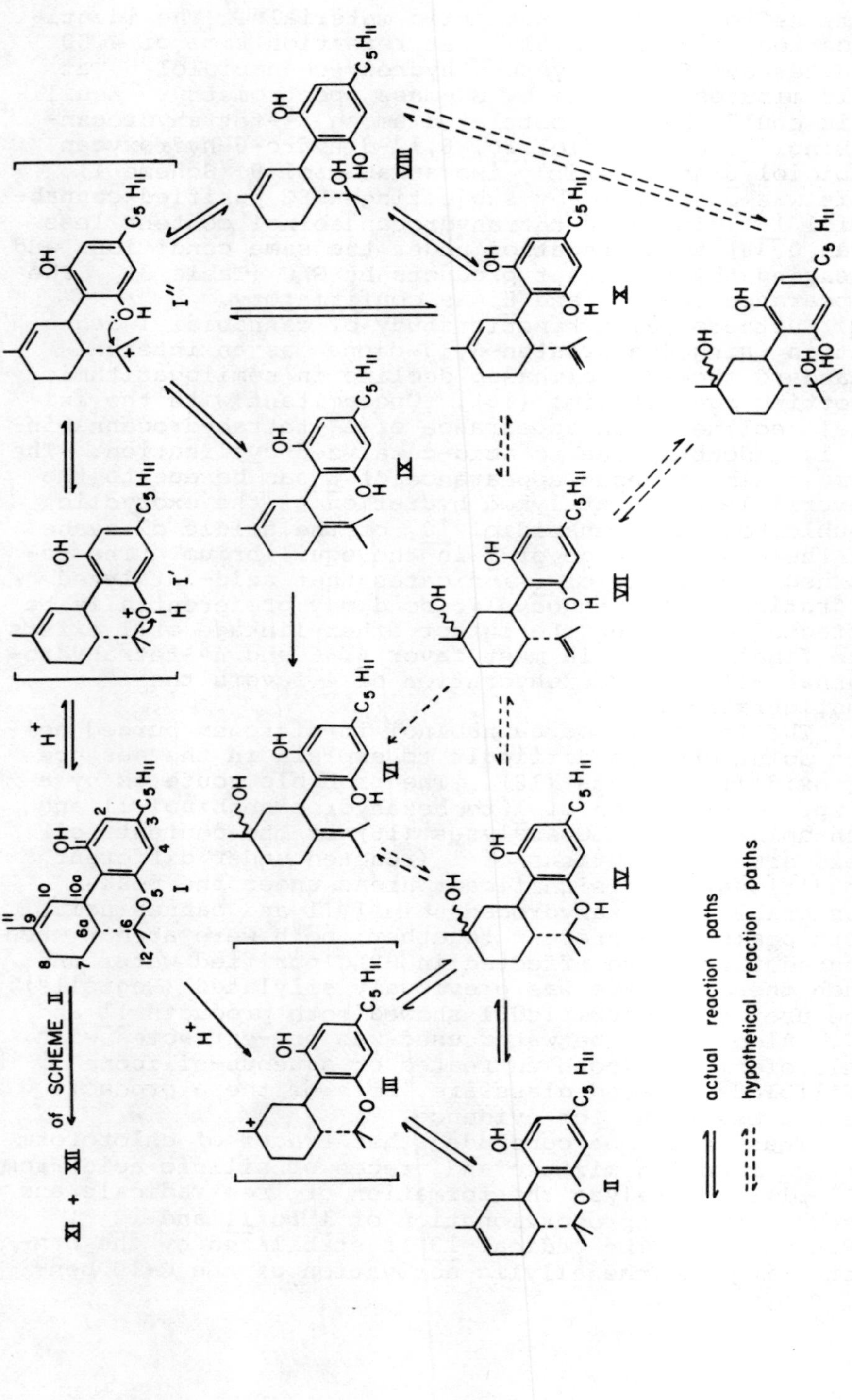

Scheme I

actual reaction paths

hypothetical reaction paths

TABLE 3

GLCa Characterization of Degradation Products from
Cannabidiol at Different pH Valuesb (From reference 16)

Compounds	Retention time (min)	Ret. time relative to the steroid	Percent of Total Areac				
			pH 0.3	pH 1.10	pH 5.72	pH 7.03	pH 9.12
Cannabidiol 10	3.19	0.36	72.33	81.71	94.71	99.30	97.11
Hexahydrocannabinol 11	3.23	0.37	---	---	---	---	---
Δ9-Tetrahydro-cannabinol 2	3.97	0.45	5.65	---	---	---	---
Δ9-Tetrahydro-cannabinol 1	4.34	0.50	10.61	8.87	3.88	0.57	2.71
Cannabinol 12	5.48	0.63	---	1.48	1.19	---	---
9,10-Dihydro-9-hydroxy-isocannabidiol 6	6.10	0.70	8.13	1.54	---	---	---
9-Hydroxyhexahydro-cannabinol 4	6.95	0.80	0.25	---	---	---	---
unknown (7?)	7.27	0.83	0.30	---	---	---	---
6,12-Dihydro-6-hydroxy-cannabidiol 8	7.68	0.88	2.02	5.16	---	---	---
4-Androsten-3,17-dione	8.73	1.00					

a OV-17 column, 240°; injector, 290°; detector, 295°; helium, 40 ml/min; hydrogen, 30 ml/min; air, 300 ml/min.
b In aqueous HCl (pH 0.3 for 20 hrs; pH 1.1 for 3 hrs) or in 0.05 M phosphate buffer for 200 min.
c The total is not 100% since there are some minor unidentified peaks.

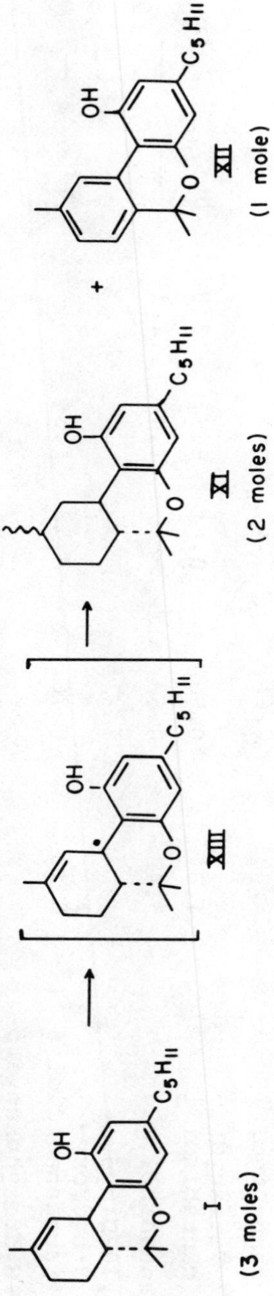

Scheme II

Equivalency of Radiochemical Analyses of ^{14}C-Δ^9-Tetrahydrocannabinol and GLC Electron Capture Detection of Derivatized Material after Normal Phase HPLC in Dog Plasma (14)

The heptane extraction efficiency from plasma was highly reproducible over a wide range of plasma concentrations(1 - 100 ng/ml): 90.6 ± 0.7% (SEM).

The recovery of 1 from the heptane extract of dog plasma by normal phase HPLC was reproducible over the range of plasma concentrations studied. Equivalent overall recoveries were obtained by both radiochemical analysis (83.7 ± 1.8% SE) and electron-capture GLC analysis (84.0 ± 4.9% SE) of the derivatized tetrahydrocannabinol.

Both methods permitted estimation of a 92.5% recovery of the amount in the heptane extract injected on HPLC and collected in the chosen range.

A similar study of the reproducibility of collection of ^{14}C-Δ^9-tetrahydrocannabinol in plasma assayed by liquid scintillation after extraction and reverse-phase HPLC was also conducted. The amounts recovered were proportional to the amounts injected, and the HPLC recovery efficiency of the drug in the heptane extract was 95.7%.

The plasma of a dog intravenously administered solutions of ^{14}C-Δ^9-tetrahydrocannabinol was monitored with time after heptane extraction by both radiochemical analysis and electron-capture GLC of the derivative of the appropriately collected eluate fraction from normal phase HPLC. Typical plots of the time course of the results from both methods are given in Figure 7.

The procedure for GLC analysis gave a lower limit for quantitation of 1 in plasma of approximately 1 ng/ml from twice the standard deviation (0.32 ng) obtained for the amount of 1 recovered from 2.25 ng in 2 ml of plasma. Similarly, the procedure for radiochemical analysis gave a lower limit of approximately 0.2 ng/ml from twice the standard deviation (0.084 ng). A statistical analysis of the apparent differences between the tetrahydrocannabinol assays at a given time from both analytical methods showed no significance.

This demonstrated that all of the recovered radioactivity from the HPLC separation procedure could be assigned to 1, assayed specifically by electron-capture GLC, and thus no significant amounts of radiolabelled metabolites were in the collected HPLC fractions.

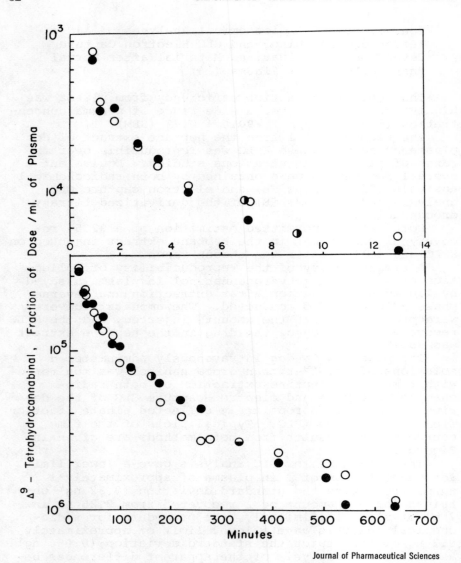

Figure 7.   Semilogarithmic plots of fraction of the Δ^9-THC, 2.0 mg/kg dose/mL of plasma, vs. time for Dog A from (○), the liquid scintillation analysis of the total ^{14}C collected as Δ^9-THC on normal-phase HPLC and from (●), the electron-capture GLC of the derivatized HPLC collected fraction. The values were corrected for the fractions of extracts and total collection range used (15).

Pharmacokinetic Studies in Dogs

When plasma suspensions of ^{14}C-Δ^9-tetrahydrocannabinol $\underline{1}$ were administered intravenously to three dogs at doses of 0.1 - 2.0 mg/kg and plasma levels of $\underline{1}$ were followed for up to 7000 minutes, no significant differences were seen in $\underline{1}$ plasma levels as determined by liquid scintillation and electron capture GLC after HPLC collection.

The time courses for the fraction of the dose per ml of plasma for each study was fit by a sum of five exponentials. The fits were not statistically different either among dogs or between doses and therefore, no dose-dependency was concluded for the dose range studied. The mean apparent volume of distribution of $\underline{1}$, referenced to total drug in plasma, $V_c = 1.31 \pm 0.07$ liters, was slightly greater than plasma volume. The mean, overall metabolic clearance, $Cl = 124.0 \pm 3$ ml/min, was approximately 50% of the estimated hepatic plasma flow, indicating that both unbound (3%) and plasma protein bound ($\approx$97%) drug were cleared by the liver. The mean, first-order metabolic rate constant, $k_M = 0.1 \pm 0.005$ min^{-1} ($t_\frac{1}{2} = 6.93 \pm 0.3$ min), demonstrated the rapid metabolism of $\underline{1}$. Return of $\underline{1}$ from tissues became the dominant rate determining process after 300 min. The mean calculated half-life of $\underline{1}$ in plasma, $t_\frac{1}{2} = 8.2 \pm 0.23$ days, was a result of a slow return of $\underline{1}$ from tissues and resulted from a substantial accumulation of $\underline{1}$ in deep compartments. An average of 24% of the dose remained unmetabolized in tissues after 5 days.

An insignificant amount of $\underline{1}$ (0.01%) was eliminated unchanged. The major fraction of the dose (40 - 45%) was eliminated as metabolites in feces within 5 days, with 14 - 16.5% eliminated as metabolites in urine for the same interval. When the bile duct of one of the dogs was cannulated and no bile was allowed to recirculate, 55% of the dose was eliminated as metabolites in bile within 5 days, indicating an enterohepatic recirculation of 10 - 15% of the dose as metabolites.

Intravenously administered biliary metabolites were rapidly eliminated in both bile and urine, supporting the proposition that the return of $\underline{1}$ from tissues was the rate determining step process after initial distribution.

CONCLUSIONS

It is clear that all relevant physicochemical properties of a drug should be obtained prior to initiating
detailed pharmacokinetic investigations (3).

The extremely low solubility of 1 (2.8 mg/l in
water and 0.77 mg/l in 0.15 M NaCl at 23°) must certainly affect its bioavailability on oral dosing of
amounts wherein the solubility is exceeded. Tetrahydrocannabinol in excess of its solubility instanta-
neously forms a stable emulsion or micellar dispersion.
Advantage can be taken of the high protein binding of 1
to administer plasma-solubilized solutions of 1 intravenously.

The rapid diffusion of Δ^9-tetrahydrocannabinol into
the plastic of containers and into the rubber stoppers
normally used as closures for plasma vials (70 - 96%)
and the significant binding to glass at low tetrahydrocannabinol concentrations (20 and 40% at 0.1 and 0.05
μg/ml, respectively, in 50 ml volumetric flasks) defi-
nitely demand careful techniques in the handling,
storage, and assay of this compound from aqueous and
biological fluids. In fact, the results of any pertinent study where these conditions were not held in
account should be quantitatively suspect.

The high degree of partition into lipid phases and
of absorption to all and any surface by tetrahydrocannabinol (lipoprotein binding may be included in
these categories) implies that oral administration of
the drug in lipid vehicles that are relatively immis-
cible with aqueous fluids would drastically reduce the
bioavailability of the drug. A common practice of ad-
ministering tetrahydrocannabinol admixed with lipid-
containing feed in animal experiments would cast sus-
picion on the dose-response relationships proposed
from the results of such studies.

The high sequestering and binding of Δ^9-tetra-
hydrocannabinol are consistent with the proposal of a
pharmacokinetically deep compartment, especially with
the known rapidity of its metabolism. The prolonged
but lowered blood levels of administered drug (17) must
be rationalized by its slow rate-determining release
from such compartments. The lack of significant renal
excretion of unchanged drug (17) is readily understand-
able since its high lipophilicity should result in
complete tubular reabsorption.

The partitioning of tetrahydrocannabinol from plasma water into red blood cells is enormously high since
D = 12.5. This may also be ascribed to the high sur-

face affinity of the drug. However, the competition of
a large degree of unsaturable binding (97%) to plasma
proteins minimizes the amounts in the red blood cells
of whole blood, although possibly large adherence of
the drug to the walls of blood vessels and to the sur-
faces of the tissues must be anticipated. The fact
that the plasma binding is largely assigned to the
lipoprotein fraction (14) may result in large individual and species variations in lipoprotein and fat content. Thus, the proposed method (7) of variable plasma
concentration may be useful in the routine determination of protein binding of individual subjects.

The large instability of Δ^9-tetrahydrocannabinol in
acid solution (16,18), implies that the drug may be
significantly degraded in the normal stomach. Again,
this intimates that oral administration may not be an
optimum route on which to establish dose-response cor-
relations. Furthermore, the choice of a cannabinoid
as an internal standard is very critical since it must
not give any interference with the other related compounds, unless a HPLC purification step is included in
the procedure. Cannabinol which, at times, has been
taken as a possible metabolite (19-21) of Δ^9-tetrahy-
drocannabinol, may only be an artifact of the analytical procedure since disproportionation of $\underline{1}$ occurs
readily.

Δ^9-Tetrahydrocannabinol can be extracted from
plasma and other biological fluids. It can be separated on HPLC from the simultaneously extracted biolog-
ically endogenous materials and metabolites that would
interfere with a chosen highly sensitive analytical
method, such as electron-capture gas liquid chromatography. It is not necessary to collect all the material to be analyzed; assurance that a reproducible or
known fraction of the total material injected on HPLC
is recovered is all that is necessary since it is
directly proportional to the total drug concentration.
If unlabelled tetrahydrocannabinol in a solution of
plasma were analyzed, the calculated recovery of known
amounts of labelled tetrahydrocannabinol added either
to plasma prior to extraction or to heptane extract
subsequent to extraction would permit calculation of
the extraction and/or HPLC collection efficiencies for
that particular biological sample. These known efficiencies would permit the calculation of the original
plasma concentrations. If a labelled ^{14}C-Δ^9-tetrahy-
drocannabinol were used in pharmacokinetic studies,
extracted and separated on the HPLC, a tritium-labelled
^3H-Δ^9-tetrahydrocannabinol could be used as the appro-
priāte internal standard to monitor recover efficiencies.

Finally, the combined use of HPLC techniques and GLC methodologies have given the same result as the radioactivity monitoring during the pharmacokinetic studies, based upon the knowledge of the physiocochemical properties of Δ^9-tetrahydrocannabinol.

ACKNOWLEDGMENTS

Supported in part by grants IRO3 MH 19268, DA-00743-01 and DA-0073 from the National Institute of Mental Health, Bethesda, Md. 20014 and in part by a NATO grant for one of us (AJG).

REFERENCES

(1)   (a) To whom inquiries should be directed;
       (b) Postdoctoral fellow from C.E.R.C.O.A.-
            C.N.R.S., 2 ā 8, Avenue Henri, Dunant,
            94320, Thiais (France);
       (c) School of Pharmacy, University of Califor-
            nia, San Francisco, CA. 94143.
(2)   Braude, M. C., *Acta Pharm. Suecica 8,* 674   (1971).
(3)   Garrett, E. R., *Int. J. Clin. Pharmacol. Ther.
       Toxicol. 4,* 6   (1970).
(4)   Lemberger, L., Silberstein, S. D., Axelrod, D.,
       and I. J. Kopin, *Science 170,* 1320   (1970).
(5)   Lemberger, L., Tamarkin, N. R., Axelrod, J.,
       and I. J. Kopin, *Science 173,* 72, (1971).
(6)   Lemberger, L., Crabtree, R. E., and H. M. Rowe,
       Science 177, 62   (1972).
(7)   Garrett, E. R., and Hunt, C. A., *J. Pharm. Sci.
       63,* 1056   (1974).
(8)   Freudenthal, R. I., Martin, J., and Wall, M. E.,
       Brit. J. Pharmacol. 44, 244   (1972).
(9)   Borgen, L. A., and Davis, W. M., *J. Pharm. Sci.
       62,* 479   (1973).
(10)   Peres-Reyes, M., Lipton, M. A., Timmons, M. C.,
       Wall, M. E., Brine, D. R., and Davis, K. H.,
       Clin. Pharmacol. Ther. 14, 48   (1973).
(11)   Saad, H. Y., and Higuchi, W. I., *J. Pharm. Sci.
       54,* 1205   (1965).
(12)   Martin, A. N., Swarbrick, J., and Cammarata, A.,
       "Physical Pharmacy", Lea and Febiger, Philadel-
       phia, Pa., 1969, p. 237.
(13)   Kortum, G., Vogel, W., and Andrussow, K., "Dis-
       sociation Constants of Organic Acids in Aqueous
       Solution", International Union of Pure and
       Applied Chemistry, Butterworth, London, England,
       1961.
(14)   Wahlquist, M., Nilsson, I. M., Sandberg, F., and
       Agurell, S., *Biochem. Pharmacol. 19,* 2579   (1970).

(15) Garrett, E. R., and Hunt, C. A., *J. Pharm. Sci.* *66*, 20 (1977).

(16) Garrett, E. R., Gouyette, A. J., and Roseboom, H., *J. Pharm. Sci.*, submitted (1977).

(17) Garrett, E. R., and Hunt, C. A., *J. Pharm. Sci.* *62*, 1211 (1973).

(18) Garrett, E. R., and Tsau, T., *J. Pharm. Sci. 63*, 1563 (1974).

(19) McCallum, N. K., *J. Chromatogr. 11*, 509 (1973).

(20) McCallum, N. K., Yagen, B., Levy, S., and Mechoulam, R., *Experientia 31*, 520 (1975).

(21) Widman, M., Nordquist, M., Agurell, S., Lindgren, J. E. and Sandberg, F., *Biochem. Pharmacol. 23*, 163 (1974).

(22) Fetterman, R. S., and Turner, C. E., *J. Pharm. Sci. 61*, 1476 (1972).

(23) Turner, C. E., and Hadley, K. W., *J. Pharm. Sci. 62*, 251 and 1083 (1973).

(24) Turner, C. E., Hadley, K. W., Henry, J., and Mole, M. L., *J. Pharm. Sci. 63*, 1872 (1974).

RECEIVED December 12, 1978.

3

Detection and Quantitation of Tetrahydrocannabinol in Physiological Fluids

MONROE E. WALL, DOLORES R. BRINE, JOAN T. BURSEY, and DAVID ROSENTHAL

Chemistry and Life Sciences Division, Research Triangle Institute, P. O. Box 12194, Research Triangle Park, NC 27709

In recent years there has been a great increase in interest in the pharmacology, metabolism and biodisposition of the cannabinoids; for recent reviews cf. Mechoulam (1), Paton and Crown (2), Wall (3) and Wall et al. (4). Until recently, quantitation of the various cannabinoids in blood, urine, feces and other biological tissues could be carried out only by the use of appropriately radio-labeled analogs of the cannabinoids under study (4, 5). Because of the widespread and increasing opposition to the use of radio-labeled isotopes in studies involving man and because many of the studies currently being conducted with various cannabinoids involve large scale experiments in which radio-labeled cannabinoids are not used, the need for the development of non-radio-labeled quantitative methodology for certain key cannabinoids has become increasingly apparent. In addition, radio-labeled thin layer chromatography techniques, while useful in initial studies, lack sufficient accuracy. When biological extracts are studied by radio-labeled means, separation of Δ^9-THC from cannabinol and of 11-hydroxy-Δ^9-THC from other monohydroxylated analogs is poor. If such interfering substances are present in considerable quantity, one will obtain erroneously high values. This will increasingly be the

0-8412-0488-8/79/47-098-039$05.00/0

case when one is analyzing biological materials obtained from marijuana smokers which contain Δ^9-THC,
cannabinol, cannabidiol, and 11-hydroxylated analogs
of these compounds.
    Quantitative gas liquid chromatography combined
with mass spectrometry (GLC-MS) has been used with excellent results for the quantitative analysis of drugs
in biological materials, combining as it does the sep-
arative powers of GLC and the inherent sensitivity of
MS detection. Pioneer studies by Hammar and Holmstedt
(6) introduced the concept of mass fragmentography (now
also called multiple ion detection (MID)) and greatly
increased the sensitivity of MS methodology so that it
could be applied to the nanogram and picogram levels.
The concept has been applied to many drugs including
a recent use by Agurell, Holmstedt and co-workers (7)
in the determination of Δ^9-THC in blood and plasma.
The application of GLC-MS techniques to the in vitro
and in vivo metabolism of Δ^9-THC (8) laid the ground-
work for the quantitative analysis of other cannabinoid
metabolites. The sites of metabolic hydroxylation for
many cannabinoids are shown in Figure 1.

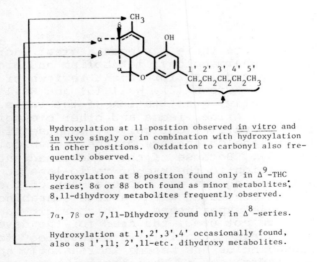

Hydroxylation at 11 position observed in vitro and
in vivo singly or in combination with hydroxylation
in other positions. Oxidation to carbonyl also frequently observed.

Hydroxylation at 8 position found only in Δ^9-THC
series; 8α or 8β both found as minor metabolites;
8,11-dihydroxy metabolites frequently observed.

7α, 7β or 7,11-Dihydroxy found only in Δ^8-series.

Hydroxylation at 1',2',3',4' occasionally found,
also as 1',11; 2',11-etc. dihydroxy metabolites.

Figure 1.   Hydroxylation sites of cannabinoids observed in vitro or in vivo

    A detailed discussion of many alternate methods
for the quantitative determination of Δ^9-THC and some
of its metabolites has been presented previously (9).
This paper will deal with determination of Δ^9-THC, 11-
hydroxy-Δ^9-THC and cannabinol in blood with one extrac-

tion. In addition, details will be presented for the determination of 11-nor-Δ^9-THC-9-carboxylic acid in blood and urine. The latter metabolite is gaining increased importance in forensic determinations.

METHODS FOR Δ^9-THC, CANNABINOL, AND 11-OH-Δ^9-THC

Clinical Protocol

Human, male volunteers who were experienced marijuana users were administered 4.0-5.0 mg of Δ^9-THC by the intravenous method of Perez-Reyes et al. (10). The volunteers were kept under medical supervision for 24 hours in the Clinical Research Unit of the University of North Carolina, School of Medicine. Blood samples (approximately 10 ml) were collected at periodic intervals over 24 hours. Plasma was obtained by centrifugation, frozen immediately and stored in frozen condition until analyzed.

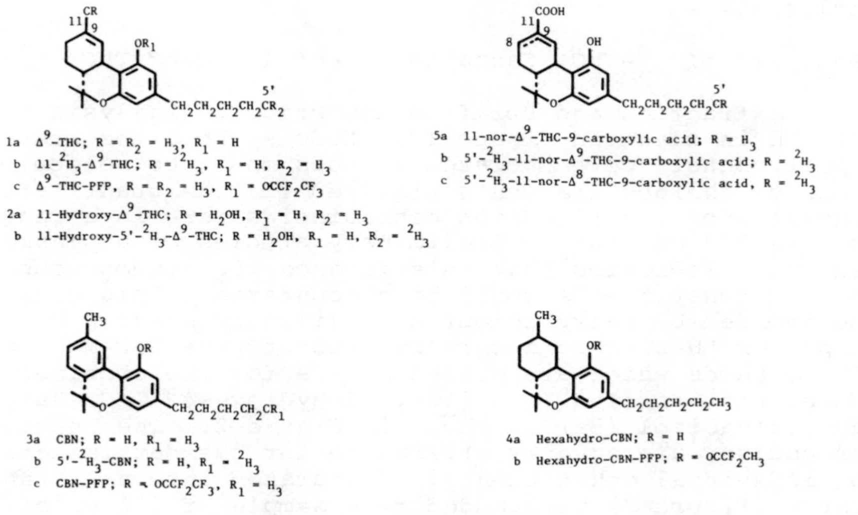

1a Δ^9-THC; R = R$_2$ = H$_3$; R$_1$ = H
 b 11-^{2}H$_3$-Δ^9-THC; R = ^{2}H$_3$, R$_1$ = H, R$_2$ = H$_3$
 c Δ^9-THC-PFP, R = R$_2$ = H$_3$, R$_1$ = OCCF$_2$CF$_3$
2a 11-Hydroxy-Δ^9-THC; R = H$_2$OH, R$_1$ = H, R$_2$ = H$_3$
 b 11-Hydroxy-5'-^{2}H$_3$-Δ^9-THC; R = H$_2$OH, R$_1$ = H, R$_2$ = ^{2}H$_3$

5a 11-nor-Δ^9-THC-9-carboxylic acid; R = H$_3$
 b 5'-^{2}H$_3$-11-nor-Δ^9-THC-9-carboxylic acid; R = ^{2}H$_3$
 c 5'-^{2}H$_3$-11-nor-Δ^8-THC-9-carboxylic acid, R = ^{2}H$_3$

3a CBN; R = H, R$_1$ = H$_3$
 b 5'-^{2}H$_3$-CBN; R = H, R$_1$ = ^{2}H$_3$
 c CBN-PFP; R = OCCF$_2$CF$_3$, R$_1$ = H$_3$

4a Hexahydro-CBN; R = H
 b Hexahydro-CBN-PFP; R = OCCF$_2$CH$_3$

Figure 2. Structure of cannabinoids and internal standards

Internal Standards

A key feature of our quantitative procedures was the use of appropriate deuterated analogs of the cannabinoids under study as both carriers for the small quantity of cannabinoids expected to be present in many cases and as internal standards for quantitation by

mass spectrometry. The structures of the cannabinoids
and their deuterated analogs used in these studies are
shown in Figure 2. All of the compounds used were synthetic and were made available by the National Institute
on Drug Abuse Synthesis Program.[1] Synthetic methods
for the various deuterated cannabinoids utilized in
these studies have been presented by Pitt et al. (11).

General Precautions

Close attention must be paid to the procedural details presented below in order to obtain reproducible
and quantitative data. In general, in working with
cannabinoids, exposure of samples or extracts to light
or air should be minimized. All solvent evaporations
should be conducted in vacuo or under nitrogen at low
temperature. Cannabinoids in nanogram levels are subject to adsorption on the surface of glassware. In
order to minimize this problem all glassware, including
chromatography columns, was silanized using 5% DMCS in
toluene.

Analysis of Δ^9-THC, Cannabinol, and 11-OH-Δ^9-THC

Extraction and Purification Prior to Analysis by
GLC-MS in electron impact (EI) Mode -- When the mass
spectrometers were operated in this mode the molecular
ions or charged fragments utilized for the quantitative
analysis of underivatized cannabinoids were in a range
of m/e 320 or lower. Preliminary studies with plasma
extracts indicated that interference from endogenous
plasma constituents would be encountered. This could
be avoided by carrying out a preliminary cleanup by
Sephadex LH-20 chromatography prior to the GLC-MS step.
The methods which are presented are for the combined
determination of Δ^9-THC (1a), 11-hydroxy-Δ^9-THC (2a),
and cannabinol (3a) as shown in Figure 2. The methods,
of course, are equally utilizable for the determination
of individual constituents. Deuterated internal standards (Figure 2) were added to a sample of 3.0 ml of
cold (not frozen) plasma as follows: 1b, 150.0 ng;
2b, 15.0 ng; and 3b, 1.50 ng. Each internal standard

Research Triangle Institute Contract HSM-42-71-95.
Qualified investigators may obtain labeled and unlabeled
cannabinoids by application to Dr. Robert Willette, Act-
ing Chief, The Research Technology Branch, Division of
Research, NIDA, Rockwall Building, 11400 Rockville Pike,
Rockville, Maryland 20852.

was added in 15-30 µl ethanol. Following addition of
each internal standard the plasma sample was stirred
for 3-5 seconds in a vortex agitator and then subjected
to sonication (Cole-Parmer ultrasonic cleaner) for the
same time. The plasma samples (contained in a screw
capped centrifuge tube) were then extracted 3 times
with 6.0 ml petroleum ether (bp 30-60°, Nanogram Grade
or Burdick and Jackson) containing 1.5% isoamyl alcohol. The tubes were agitated 15 minutes each time in
a vortex agitator and the layers separated by centrifugation after each extraction. The petroleum ether
extracts were combined, evaporated in vacuo at room
temperature and freeze dried overnight to remove water
and isoamyl alcohol. The dried residue was dissolved
in a minimal volume of petroleum ether/chloroform/etha-
nol (10:10:1) and chromatographed in the same solvent
mixture on 1 x 40 cm water jacketed Sephadex LH-20
columns at 26°C. Twenty-seven ml of column eluant were
collected and discarded. Seven ml of eluant was then
collected as the fraction containing Δ^9-THC. The next
8 ml of eluant was collected as the CBN-containing
fraction. Thirty-eight ml of column effluent was then
collected and discarded. Finally, 17 ml of eluant was
collected as the fraction containing 11-hydroxy-Δ^9-THC.
The Δ^9-THC and CBN fractions were evaporated to dryness
and dissolved in 30 µl hexane. The 11-hydroxy-Δ^9-THC
fraction was evaporated to dryness under vacuum and
heated with 75 µl of Regisil (BSTFA + 1% TCMS) in a
closed vial at 110° for 3 hours. The reagent was removed in vacuum and the residue dissolved in 20 µl hexane.
     Gas Chromatography Conditions -- On the LKB-9000
GLC-MS a 3' or 6' x 1/4" glass column of 2% OV-17 on
Chromosorb W-HP (80/100 mesh) was utilized, the former
length being used for 11-hydroxy-Δ^9-THC-bis-TMS ether
(at 220°C) and the latter length for both Δ^9-THC (at
220°C) and CBN (at 240°C). Helium was used as the gas
phase at a rate of 35 ml/min. Under the conditions
stipulated above, retention times of 4-6 minutes were
observed for each compound. Only Δ^9-THC and CBN were
analyzed on the Finnigan 3300 instrument in the EI mode.
Six foot glass columns containing 1% SE-30 on 100/120
mesh Chromosorb W-HP were used at column temperatures
of 200-230°C and the flow of 30-35 ml/min.
     Mass Spectrometry -- The mass spectrometers and
associated equipment have been described in detail
(9). In brief, an LKB 9000 GLC-MS (a magnetic sector
instrument) was utilized with a modified accelerating
voltage alternator (AVA) (12). For Δ^9-THC the mass
spectrometer was set to focus alternately on the ions

m/e 314 and 317 which correspond to the molecular ion
of the compound and its trideutero analog. For CBN
the molecular ions were m/e 310 and 313. For analysis
of 11-hydroxy-Δ^9-THC as the bis-TMS ether, the strong
M-103 ion (8, 13) at m/e 371 and 374 was selected.
The AVA accessory measures the two peak heights or areas
utilized for each analysis as described above. Alter-
natively the Finnigan 3300 GLC/MS (a quadrupole instrument) with a dedicated PDP-12 computer (9) was utilized,
and the ratios of peak heights or areas were determined
using computer software.

TLC-Radio-label Procedure -- The volunteer subjects
(described in Clinical Protocol) all received 100 μCi
of tritium labeled Δ^9-THC, along with the standard 4.0-
5.0 mg intravenous dose. Two to three ml aliquots of
plasma were analyzed by the procedure described by Wall
(4).

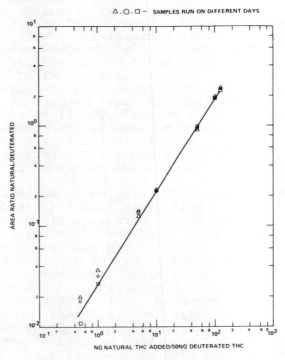

Figure 3.   Finnigan 3300-EI plasma calibration curve for Δ^9-THC

RESULTS FOR Δ^9-THC, CANNABINOL, AND 11-OH-Δ^9-THC

Plasma calibration curves obtained with the LKB

and Finnigan GLC-MS instruments were quite similar for both Δ^9-THC and cannabinol. For Δ^9-THC linear calibration curves in the range of 1-100 ng/ml of plasma were obtained with both instruments. Figure 3 shows data for the Finnigan. Detection of Δ^9-THC down to 0.1 ng/ml could be attained, but 0.5 ng/ml is regarded as the minimal concentration at which reliable data could be obtained. Plasma calibration curves for CBN are exemplified for the Finnigan MS in Figure 4; the LKB data was similar. Linear curves on both instruments were obtained between 0.2-10.0 ng/ml with detection limits about 0.1 ng/ml. Only the LKB 9000 MS was used for the 11-hydroxy-Δ^9-THC determinations. The data are shown in Figure 5. The curve was linear in the range of 0.2-10.0 ng/ml plasma of 11-hydroxy metabolite.

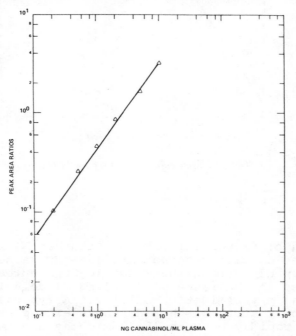

Figure 4.   Finnigan 3300-EI plasma calibration curve for CBN

Figure 6 presents the average values with standard error obtained for Δ^9-THC, 11-OH-Δ^9-THC and cannabinol from plasma of male volunteers receiving Δ^9-THC by intravenous infusion. The measurements covered a 24 hour period. Δ^9-THC values obtained with the LKB-9000 EI source were in close agreement with the data obtained on the Finnigan 3300 chemical ionization (CI) source.

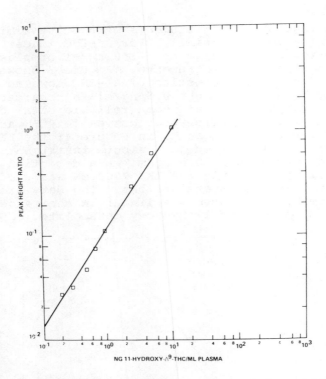

Figure 5.   LKB 9000-EI plasma calibration curve for 11-hydroxy-Δ^9-THC

Comparison of values for LKB vs. Finnigan EI source
also showed excellent agreement. Δ^9-THC values increased rapidly during the first 10-20 minutes, the
peak values in the range of 50-60 ng/ml coinciding with
the maximal psychomimetic activity. A typical biphasic
elimination pattern was noted; the Δ^9-THC plasma levels
decreased rapidly between 15-40 minutes and then fell
at a much slower rate. With a particular group of
volunteers (3 subjects) levels after 24 hours were between 3-5 ng/ml. Spot checks at lower levels utilizing
the Finnigan MID program confirmed that the substance
being evaluated was indeed Δ^9-THC and not instrument
"noise." In the case of 11-hydroxy-Δ^9-THC much lower
levels were found. Peak values in the neighborhood of
2.0 ng/ml were noted between 30-40 minutes. The maximal values declined in a more gradual manner than was

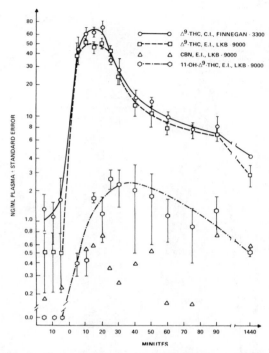

Figure 6.   Plasma levels of Δ⁹-THC, 11-hydroxy-Δ⁹-THC, and CBN found over a 24-hr period in human plasma from volunteers receiving Δ⁹-THC by iv administration

the case for Δ^9-THC, falling to a level of 1.0 ng/ml in 60-90 minutes and 0.5 ng/ml after 24 hours. The values for CBN shown in Figure 6 have no pharmacokinetic significance as most of the data falls below the level of analytical reliability.

Figure 7 compares the results obtained from the average of four subjects analyzed by GLC-MS-EI, TLC, radio-label, and electron capture GLC. Correlation coefficients are calculated in Figure 8. The results are in reasonable agreement, and in particular the GLC-MS and electron capture GLC procedures gave good agreement for most points over the whole curve.

METHODS FOR 11-NOR-Δ^9-THC-9-CARBOXYLIC ACID

Extraction and Purification

Following the addition of 300 ng of deuterated internal standard (5c, cf. Fig. 2) to 3.0 ml of cold plasma or urine, the sample was sonicated with 30 ml

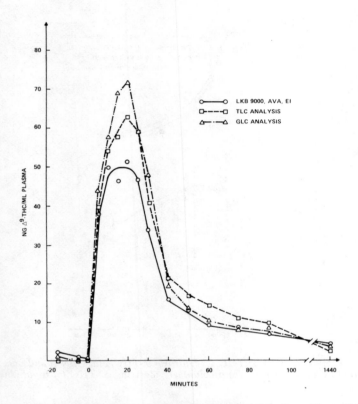

Figure 7.   The Δ⁹-THC found in plasma following administration of 5 mg Δ⁹-THC
(average of 4 subjects)

acetone for 30 minutes. The sample was centrifuged
to remove precipitated proteins, the acetone decanted,
and the pellet re-extracted with an additional 30 ml
acetone. Acetone extracts were combined and concentrated in vacuo to an aqueous residue. The volume was
adjusted to 3.0 ml with distilled water and the pH to
3. The cannabinoid acids were extracted from the aqueous phase by two partitions with 10 ml of diethyl
ether. This was accomplished by agitating the centrifuge tubes 15 minutes each time in a vortex agitator
and separating the phases by centrifugation. The diethyl ether extracts were combined, evaporated in
vacuo, re-dissolved in 0.5 ml methanol, and filtered
through a 5 micron teflon filter.

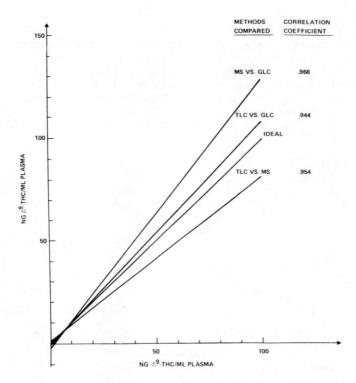

Figure 8. Least-squares best lines comparing all data obtained by each of two methods of analysis

The extracts thus obtained were purified by high performance liquid chromatography (HPLC) on a reverse phase μ-C_{18} (Partisil-20) column (30 cm x 4.6 mm ID) using a methanol/water mobile phase (65:35, containing 0.05% ammonium acetate). At a flow rate of 4 ml/min. the mixture of 5a and deuterated internal standard 5c were eluted at a time interval of 8-13 minutes. This fraction of eluant was collected and freeze dried. The residue was transferred to a half dram vial and dried in vacuo overnight with 10 mg of potassium carbonate. Under anhydrous conditions 0.2 ml dry acetone and 8 μl dimethyl sulfate were added to the sample. The vial was tightly capped and heated with shaking at 50°C for 6 hours. Following the addition of 0.5 ml distilled water to each sample, the derivatized cannabinoids were removed by two extractions with 0.5 ml chloroform. The chloroform was evaporated under nitrogen and the residue re-dissolved in 30 μl chloroform.

GLC-MS Analysis

The dimethylated derivatives of the mixture of 5a
and 5c were submitted to analysis on the LKB-9000 GLC-
MS with AVA described previously. Samples were chromatographed at 250°C on a 6' column of OV-17, 2%, on
Supelcoport (80/100 mesh) with a He carrier gas flow
rate of 30 ml/minute. The ratio of the peak heights at
m/e 372 and 375 was determined in the usual manner.

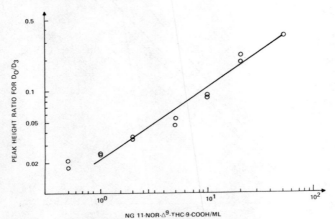

Figure 9. *Instrument calibration for 11-nor-Δ^9-THC-9-COOH extracted from
human plasma*

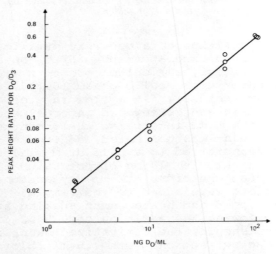

Figure 10. *Instrument calibration curve for 11-nor-Δ^9-THC-9-COOH in human
urine*

RESULTS FOR 11-NOR-Δ^9-THC-9-CARBOXYLIC ACID

A plasma calibration curve for 11-nor-Δ^9-THC-9-carboxylic acid, 5a, is shown in Figure 9. There was reasonable linearity from 1.0-50 ng/ml plasma with detection limits of 0.5 ng or less per ml. Figure 10 presents similar data for a urine calibration curve. The method showed reasonable linearity between 2.0-100 ng/ml urine. Figure 11 presents pharmacokinetic data for plasma levels of a human volunteer, BS, over a 0.5 hour to 48 hour period comparing Δ^9-THC and 11-nor acid levels after a dose of 5.0 mg of Δ^9-THC by the intravenous route. Both parent compound and acid metabolite exhibited a biphasic elimination pattern although the levels of the acid did not fall as rapidly as parent compound. Elimination of the acid metabolite 5a in urine is shown in Figure 12. It is evident that urinary elimination proceeded rapidly as 80% of the total 11-nor-acid excreted was eliminated in the urine during

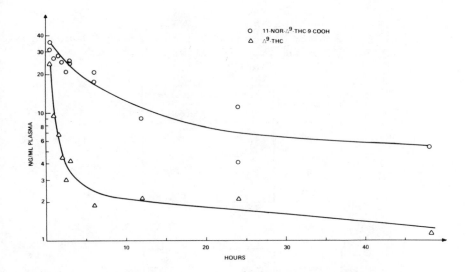

Figure 11. The Δ^9-THC and 11-nor-Δ^9-THC-9-COOH excreted in the urine of subject BS after iv infusion of 4 mg Δ^9-THC

the first 6 hours after administration of parent compound; further elimination proceeded much more slowly. Table 1 compares results obtained by TLC assay (4) and the GLC-MS procedure in urine and plasma of subject BS. Agreement was excellent in most of the cases.

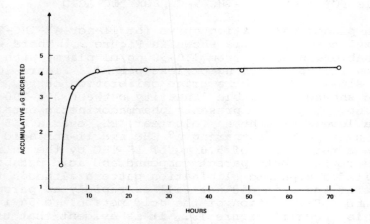

Figure 12.   The 11-nor-Δ⁹-THC-9-COOH excreted in the urine of subject BS after
iv infusion of 4 mg Δ⁹-THC

Table 1
Comparison of GLC-MS and TLC Analysis of 11-nor-Δ⁹-THC-9-COOH in the Plasma and Urine of Subject BS.

minutes	ng/ml plasma found by	
	tlc	glc-ms
30	36	36
60	30	27
90	32	28
120	35	25

hours	ng/ml urine found by	
	tlc	glc-ms
3	7.4	5.4
6	15	22
12	6.7	6.2
24	2.1	.2
48	1.0	--
72	0.89	.2

DISCUSSION

The basic objective of this investigation was to establish sensitive methodology which would not depend on radio-labeling for the quantitative estimation of Δ^9-THC, its primary metabolite 11-hydroxy-Δ^9-THC (3), and cannabinol, which has been reported to be a metabolite of Δ^9-THC in the rat (14). This objective has been realized, utilizing GLC-MS with a variety of techniques and instruments. In addition, the quantitative estimation of 11-nor-Δ^9-THC-9-carboxylic acid has been accomplished. Several aspects of our results merit further discussion.

Choice of Instrument

Two completely different types of mass spectrometers coupled with different means for quantitation of data were utilized. One was a relatively old (1968) magnetic sector MS, the LKB-9000, which was coupled with an accelerating voltage alternator which permitted measurement of the ratio of the peak height of the unknown as compared with that of the internal standard. The other was a newer (1974) quadrupole MS, the Finnigan 3300, which was interfaced to a PDP-12 computer. The Finnigan MS has both EI and CI sources. As shown in the Results section, both instruments in the EI mode gave virtually identical plasma calibration curves with identical linear range and quite similar standard error of estimation. Figure 6 gives pharmacokinetic data in man obtained on the LKB in the EI mode and the Finnigan in the CI mode. The results are quite similar. It is thus evident that a wide variety of mass spectrometers can be used with comparable results provided appropriate internal carriers and standards are added. Before concluding this discussion one word of caution should be given. The nature of the separators is most important; the LKB with the Ryhage separator and the Finnigan with a silylated glass jet separator gave appropriate sensitivity. On the other hand, another mass spectrometer which utilized a Watson-Biemann separator showed poor sensitivity and could not be utilized for cannabinoid studies.

Internal Standards

As indicated previously, the final mass spectrometric measurements can be conducted with great accuracy. The key to success in the various analytical studies was the utilization of appropriate compounds which could be employed as both carriers and internal standards.

For this purpose deuterium labeled cannabinoids identical to the parent compound except for the label are
ideal and were utilized for all of the EI studies. It
is possible to use with equal success an internal carrier which is not isotopically labeled as long as its
properties are very similar to that of the cannabinoid
being studied but permit separation by GLC. Hexahydrocannabinol was excellent for this purpose and was used
in CI studies of Δ^9-THC and cannabinol.

The Analysis for 11-Nor-Δ^9-THC-9-Carboxylic Acid (5a)

The analysis for this "end" metabolite of Δ^9-THC
caused particular problems. Especially baffling for a
considerable time was the analysis of 5a in plasma.
This was finally solved by the realization that 5a in
plasma or urine containing blood (in cases of illness
or injury) is probably non-covalently bonded to a protein. As a result, although this combination is ether
extractable, it remains bound and passes through the re-
quisite HPLC purification step at a retention time markedly different than pure 5a. It was found that treatment of the "protein"-5a complex with acetone precipitated the plasma proteins and broke up the "protein"-5a
complex. Other points of interest were the requirement
for derivatization of 5a as the methyl ester of the carboxylic acid and the methyl ether of the phenolic hydroxyl moiety. Bis-silylation of these functions was
not quantitative. The Δ^8-deuterated analog 5a is
more readily available than the Δ^9-deuterated analog 5b.
Recently the latter has been synthesized (11, 16). No
advantage in precision or sensitivity was noted in using
5b in preference to 5c.

Metabolic and Pharmacokinetic Data

The development of sensitive and accurate GLC-MS
methodology permitted a preliminary study in man utilizing these techniques for the precise determination of
Δ^9-THC, 11-hydroxy-Δ^9-THC and CBN in plasma. Previously
we have made an extensive study (4) of the metabolism
of Δ^9-THC in man using radio-labeled tracers and thin
layer chromatography. The procedures utilized (in addition to the undesirability of a radio-labeled tracer
in man) suffer from two potential sources of error.
The method would not permit separation of Δ^9-THC from
CBN, and in the case of 11-hydroxy-Δ^9-THC, would not
permit separation from other monohydroxy metabolites
which might be present (8, 17).
The data in Figure 6 for Δ^9-THC are quite comparable

to pharmacokinetic data obtained in earlier studies (4). In both instances a biphasic elimination curve was noted. After the initial maximum level, a sharp decline was followed by a more gradual decrease. Maximal values in the current studies were 50-60 ng/ml. After 24 hours, 3-5 ng/ml of Δ^9-THC were still found in the plasma. Our results for 11-hydroxy-Δ^9-THC are probably the most accurate data yet reported in man. The concentration of this active metabolite (Figure 6) was only 2-3 ng/ml at peak levels declining at a slower rate than Δ^9-THC to 0.5 ng/ml after 24 hours. Although Δ^9-THC is readily converted to 11-hydroxy-Δ^9-THC in the liver (3), only small quantities find their way into the blood.

Our interest in CBN was aroused by reports from McCallum (14, 15) which indicate that CBN might be a transitory metabolite found at very early time periods after administration of Δ^9-THC. As shown in Figure 6, the level of CBN was below the reliability limits in the EI mode. Other studies we have carried out by electron capture GLC or GLC-MS in the CI mode indicate the virtual absence of this substance at all time periods. Since we have found that CBN has the same general pharmacokinetic pattern as Δ^9-THC in man (4), we must conclude that CBN can be <u>disregarded</u> in terms of its importance as a metabolite in man.

We present for the first time pharmacokinetic data in plasma and urine obtained by GLC-MS for the important acid metabolite 11-nor-Δ^9-THC-9-carboxylic acid. This and related acids constitute the major means by which Δ^9-THC is excreted in the urine. The data indicate rapid elimination of the acid in the urine during the first 3-6 hours after administration of Δ^9-THC.

Comparison of GLC-MS With Other Procedures

As shown in Figures 7 and 8, the GLC-MS procedures show reasonable agreement in the case of Δ^9-THC with data obtained by two independent procedures involving, respectively, thin layer chromatography of radio-labeled cannabinoids and a double GLC-electron capture procedure. In preliminary studies on cannabinol levels of subjects who received Δ^9-THC, good agreement was found between the GLC-MS EI method, reinforcing our belief that CBN is not a significant metabolite of Δ^9-THC in man. Finally, Table 1 shows excellent agreement between the TLC-radio-labeled procedure and GLC-MS analysis for the 11-nor-acid, <u>5a</u>.

ACKNOWLEDGMENTS

These studies were conducted with the support of the National Institute on Drug Abuse under contracts HMS-41-75-95 and ADM-45-74-109. We wish to thank Mario Perez-Reyes, M.D. for clinical material used in some of these studies and express to Mrs. Valerie H. Schindler, Mr. Philip Brown Belt and Mr. Jarvey M. Taylor our appreciation for their technical assistance.

REFERENCES

(1) Mechoulam, R., Ed., "Marijuana", Academic Press, New York, New York, 1973, pp. 1-409.

(2) Paton, W. D. and Crown, J., "Cannabis and Its Derivatives", Oxford University Press, London, England, 1972, pp. 1-198.

(3) Wall, M. E. in "Recent Advances in Phytochemistry", V. C. Runeckles, Ed., Plenum Publishing Co., New York, 1975, pp. 29-61.

(4) Wall, M. E., Brine, D. R. and Perez-Reyes, M., in "Pharmacology of Marijuana", Eds. M. Braude and S. Szara, Raven Press, New York, 1976, pp. 93-116.

(5) Lemberger, L., in "Advances in Pharmacology and Chemotherapy", Eds. Garratini, S., F. Hawking, A. Golden, and I. Kopin, Academic Press, New York, 1972, p. 221.

(6) Hammar, C.-G. and Holmstedt, B., *Anal. Biochem.* *22*, 532 (1968).

(7) Agurell, S., Gustafsson, B., Holmstedt, B., Leander, K., Lindgren, J-E., Nilsson, I., Sandberg, F. and Asberg, M., *J. Pharm. Pharmac. 25*, 554 (1973).

(8) Wall, M. E., Brine, D. R. and Perez-Reyes, M., in "Marijuana: Chemistry, Biochemistry, and Cellular Effects", Ed. G. G. Nahas, Springer-Verlag, New York, 1976, pp. 51-62.

(9) Wall, M. E., Harvey, T. M., Bursey, J. T., Brine, D. R. and Rosenthal, D., in "Cannabinoid Assays in Humans", NIDA Research Monograph No. 7, 1976, pp. 107-117.

(10) Perez, Reyes, M., Timmons, M., Lipton, M., Davis, K. and Wall, M., *Science 177*, 633 (1972).

(11) Pitt, C. G., Hobbs, D. T., Schran, H., Twine, C. E. and Williams, D. L., *J. Label Comp. 11*, 551 (1975).

(12) Klein, P. D., Hauman, J. R. and Eisler, W. J., *Anal. Chem. 44*, 410 (1972).

(13) Wall, M. E., Brine, D. R., Brine, G. A., Pitt, C. G., Freudenthal, R. I. and Christensen, H. D.,

J. Amer. Chem. Soc. 92, 3466 (1970).

(14) McCallum, N. K., *Experientia 31*, 957 (1975).

(15) McCallum, N. K., Yagen, B., Levy, S. and Mechoulam, R., *Experientia 31*, 510 (1975).

(16) Pitt, C. G., Fowler, M., Sathe, S., Srivastava,
S. C. and Williams, D. L., *J. Amer. Chem. Soc.
97*, 3798 (1975).

(17) Wall, M. E. and Brine, D. R., "Summaries", International Symposium on Mass Spectrometry in
Biochemistry and Medicine, Milan, Italy, 1973,
p. 52.

RECEIVED December 12, 1978.

Quantitation of Δ^9-Tetrahydrocannabinol and 11-Nor-Δ^9-tetrahydrocannabinol-9-carboxylic Acid in Body Fluids by GC/CI–MS

R. L. FOLTZ, P. A. CLARKE, B. J. HIDY, D. C. K. LIN, A. P. GRAFFEO, and B. A. PETERSEN

Battelle Columbus Laboratories, Columbus, OH 43201

Cannabinoid analytical work in our laboratory currently consists of two major areas of activity: 1) quantitative analysis of Δ^9-THC in samples of physiological fluids submitted by outside researchers under a NIDA program, and 2) development of an ultra-sensitive method for simultaneous quantitation of Δ^9-THC and its major metabolites in body fluids.

CURRENT METHODOLOGY FOR QUANTITATION OF Δ^9-THC

The method that we are using for analysis of THC on a service basis is similar to that developed by Agurell, et. al. (1). Deuterium-labeled Δ^9-THC is added to the plasma sample, followed by extraction, treatment of the extract with a derivatizing agent, and quantitation by GC/MS analysis using the technique of selected ion monitoring. The major differences between our procedure and that developed by Agurell's group is that we use an extraction procedure similar to that reported by Wall, et. al., (2) and we use chemical ionization for our mass spectral analysis rather than electron impact ionization.

A flow diagram of our extraction procedure is shown in Figure 1. We find that this procedure provides adequate clean-up and recovery of the THC in the least amount of time (3). However, it should be stated that the degree of clean-up achieved by this procedure is adequate primarily because we are using chemical ionization mass spectrometry to measure the ratio of labeled to unlabeled Δ^9-THC. In our experience chemical ionization often affords better sensitivity and specificity than electron impact ionization. For rea-

0-8412-0488-8/79/47-098-059$05.00/0

gent gas we use a mixture of methane and ammonia. The methane is used as the GC carrier gas, and the ammonia is bled into the ion source through a make-up gas inlet.

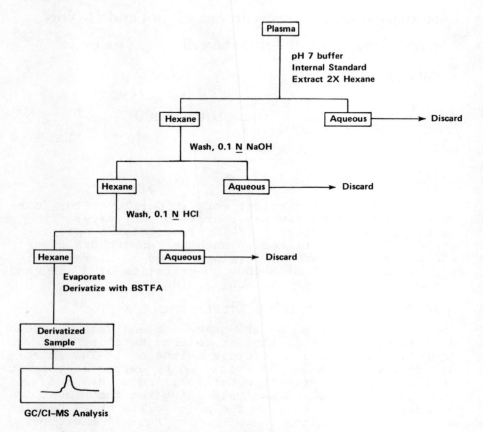

Figure 1.   Flow diagram for analysis of Δ^9-THC in physiological fluids

The reasons for our choosing this combination of reagent gases are illustrated in Figure 2 and Table 1. Figure 2 compares the EI mass spectrum of the trimethylsilyl derivative of Δ^9-THC with the corresponding CI mass spectra using methane as reagent gas and the methane ammonia combination as reagent gas. In the methane-ammonia CI mass spectrum essentially all of the THC ion current is concentrated at a single ion mass, corresponding to the protonated molecule ion (m/e 387). The sensitivities achieved by selected ion monitoring analysis of a specific quantity of Δ^9-THC are compared in

the fourth column in Table 1. These data were obtained
on two Finnigan quadrupole GC/MS systems, one optimized
for CI and the other for EI ionization. Use of methane
and ammonia gives the largest signal per unit weight
of THC. Furthermore, the absence of fragment ions in
methane-ammonia CI mass spectrum means that there is
less chance of interference from ions due to other components of the extract.

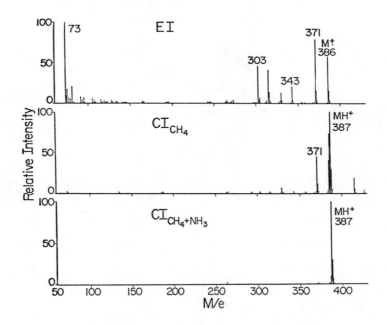

Figure 2. MS of the TMS ether of Δ^9-THC

We have found methane-ammonia chemical ionization
to be well suited for the analysis of a wide variety of
drugs (4). However, some compounds are ionized with
poor efficiency under these CI conditions, so it is important to measure the relative sensitivities afforded
by different modes cf ionization before selecting a
procedure for a given compound.

Figure 3 shows a computer plot of the ion currents
at m/e 387 and 390 corresponding to 5 ng/ml of Δ^9-THC-d_0
and 20 ng/ml of Δ^9-THC-d_3. Only about 1/10 of the
total volume of extract was injected into the GC/MS,
so that the actual quantity of Δ^9-THC-TMS-d_0 injected
on column was approximately 500 pg.

The total time required for extraction and analysis of a single sample is about 5 hours. However, we

find it most efficient for one analyst to work with the
samples in batches of 32. The complete analysis of 32
samples requires about 14 hours.

Table 1

*Relative Responses for Prominent Ions
in the EI and CI Mass Spectra of the
trimethylsilyl ether of Δ^9-
tetrahydrocannabinol.*

Mol. Wt. = 386

Ionization Method	m/e Monitored	% of Sample Ion Current	Relative Response Per Unit Weight of Δ^9-THC
EI	386 ($M^{\ddagger}$)	7	50
CI (CH_4)	387 (MH^+)	24	20
CI (CH_4+NH_3)	387 (MH^+)	67	100

The analytical method has been in operation on a
semi-routine basis for about 1-1/2 years, although we
continue to incorporate minor refinements in the procedure. During this time approximately 500 submitted
samples have been analyzed, including rat, monkey, and
human plasma in quantities ranging from 0.25 to 2 ml.
Levels of Δ^9-THC in the samples have been typically in
the 1 to 50 ng/ml range, although occasionally concentrations as high as 400 ng/ml are encountered. The
precision of the method is shown in Table 2.

We no longer establish a new standard curve prior
to analyzing each batch of samples. Instead, for every
6 unknown samples being analyzed, we include one plasma sample having a known concentration of Δ^9-THC (typically 10 ng/ml). A new standard curve is established
following any procedural or instrumental change, or
when we notice a deterioration in the accuracy of measurements obtained on the spiked samples. The standard
curves have been linear over the concentration range of
1 to 100 ng/ml and give correlation coefficients of

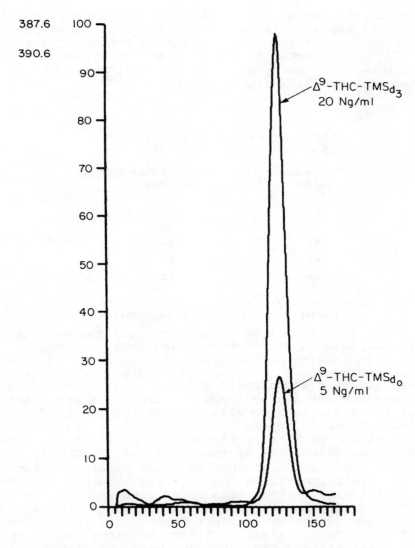

Figure 3. Selected ion monitoring plot for quantitation of Δ^9-THC

0.998 or better.

The problems that we have encountered include those which everyone who is doing quantitation of Δ^9-THC has had to face. The Δ^9-THC standard solutions are unstable. Even when the solutions are kept in sealed containers at freezer temperatures, over a period of a few months we notice a definite decrease in

the concentration of the Δ^9-THC and the appearance of
additional peaks in the SIM chromatograms. Consequently, it is necessary to measure the concentrations of
Δ^9-THC$_{d_0}$ and Δ^9-THC$_{d}$ in the standard solutions at fre-
quent intervals, using a stable internal standard such
as 4-androstene-3,17-dione.

Table 2

*Precision data for measurement
of Δ^9-THC added to plasma*

Δ^9 – THC ADDED (NG/ML)	RELATIVE STANDARD DEVIATION (%)
92	0.5
46	3.0
9.2	3.9
4.6	5.1
0.9	7.3

*4 SAMPLES ANALYZED TWICE AT EACH CONCENTRATION

Early in our work we frequently obtained erratic
analytical results which were subsequently traced to
cross-contamination between samples. In order to eliminate this source of error we instituted use of dis-
posable pipettes and adopted a far more rigorous clean-
ing procedure for that glassware which is reused. All
of our glassware is also silylated by the vapor-phase
procedure recently reported by Fenimore, et. al. (5).
We also occasionally encountered extracts in which
we could not detect any of the d_0-or d_3-Δ^9-THC-TMS.
In these cases, small amounts of water apparently got
into the vials containing the extracts prior to tri-
methylsilylation, either because of condensation during solvent evaporation, or due to accidental inclu-
sion of some of the water layer during the final transfer of the organic extract. Traces of water remaining
in the final extract can interfere with the trimethyl-
silylation. We prefer to avoid use of drying agents
for fear of losing some of the THC due to adsorption
on the drying agent. In any case, the problem can be
avoided by exercising greater care during the final
separation of organic extract from the water layer,
and by being careful to see that the temperature of the
extract is kept above room temperature during the final
evaporative concentration.

DEVELOPMENT OF A PROCEDURE FOR SIMULTANEOUS QUANTITATION OF Δ^9-THC, 11-HYDROXY-Δ^9-THC, AND 11-NOR-Δ^9-THC-9-CARBOXYLIC ACID

THC is rapidly metabolized once it enters the body, as is the case for many other drugs. In these situations it is often valuable to be able to monitor the concentrations of the metabolites as well as the parent drug. Unfortunately, significant differences in the partition coefficients of parent drugs and their more polar metabolites have prevented the development of procedures for their simultaneous extraction, clean-up, and quantitation.

The objective of our current research is to develop a single, multi-technique procedure that can be used for simultaneous quantitation of Δ^9-THC and its major metabolites at concentrations as low as 10 pg/ml of body fluid. The method consists of direct injection of the body fluid onto a reverse-phase high pressure liquid chromatographic (HPLC) column, collection of the eluent fractions containing the Δ^9-THC and its metabolites, derivatization, and quantitation using capillary gas chromatography/chemical ionization mass spectrometry. This is the basic approach that we used for quantitation of benzoyl ecgonine in urine (6). We expect that once the method is fully developed, it will be possible to use it for quantitation of a wide variety of drugs and metabolites with only minor changes in the operational parameters. It should also be possible to automate most phases of the method in order to reduce the amount of labor required and increase the method's precision.

The overall method can be described best by considering separately each of the individual techniques employed.

High Pressure Liquid Chromatography Clean-up.

High pressure liquid chromatography is used to isolate THC and its two metabolites from the bulk of the other components of body fluids due to their differences in relative retention. By direct injection of the body fluid and subsequent collection following gradient elution, THC and two of its metabolites are simultaneously extracted and significantly purified in one step.

The HPLC system we use for isolation of the THC and the two metabolites uses a μ-Bondapak-C_{18} reverse-phase column. (Waters Associates, Inc.) The column

is eluted using a water/methanol gradient. Our reason
for choosing this system is that it allows us to inject the body fluid directly onto the column. Furthermore, the retention volumes of the THC and metabolites
are highly reproducible, since they are dependent primarily on our ability to accurately reproduce the solvent gradient profile. This latter factor is very important since we are concerned with concentrations of
cannabinoids below the detectability of the UV absorption detector of the HPLC system. To permit us to
monitor the reproducibility of the gradient profile we
add a marker compound to the body fluid, along with a
deuterated analog of each of the cannabinoids to be
measured, before injection onto the column.

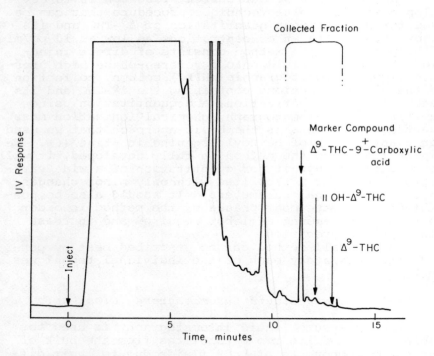

Figure 4. HPLC chromatogram of 1 mL of urine using a reverse phase column

Figure 4 shows the UV absorption chromatogram for a 1-
ml urine sample containing 20 ng of the deuterated an-
alogs of Δ^9-THC, 11-OH-Δ^9-THC, and 11-nor-Δ^9-THC-car-
boxylic acid, and 1 µg of a marker compound. In this
case the marker compound is 2-methylnaphthalene which

elutes coincident with the 11-nor-Δ^9-THC-carboxylic
acid. Since the marker compound has a molecular
weight considerably lower than the cannabinoids, it
does not interfere in any way with the GC/MS quantitation.
 Our initial attempts to use this HPLC clean-up of
urine samples prior to quantitation of the carboxy metabolite were successful down to a concentration of
5 ng/ml. At lower concentrations we obtained erratic
results. The problem was subsequently traced to partial retention of the cannabinoid in the injector,
giving rise to the so-called "ghosting" phenomenon.
We are now using a Waters Associates Model U6K injector which appears to be free of this problem.

*Concentration and Derivatization of the HPLC
Eluent.*

 After collection of the water-methanol eluent
containing the cannabinoids, it is necessary to remove
all of the methanol and water before derivatization
and GC/MS analysis. Normal evaporation under a N_2
stream is time-consuming because of the low volatility
of the water. We are now using a Buchler evaporator
for this operation. This device permits simultaneous
concentration of thirty-six 15-ml eluent fractions by
means of heating under reduced pressure while applying
a vortexing action to prevent solvent bumping. In our
limited experience with the device it appears to work
well. In a test run consisting of an intermix of
tubes containing radio-labeled and unlabeled Δ^9-THC,
we found no evidence for cross-contamination between
samples.
 After evaporation to dryness the fractions are
derivatized by heating with bis-trimethylsilyl tri-
fluoroacetamide (BSFTA) at 90°C for one hour.

Separation by Glass Capillary Gas Chromatography

 For GC/MS analysis of the derivatized fractions
we are currently using a 25 meter x 0.26 mm I.D. SE-
30 coated glass capillary column supplied by the
Quadrex Company. Although our experience with quantitative analyses using capillary columns is still
very limited, we are convinced that glass capillary
columns offer significant advantages for this type of
analysis. Specifically, the advantages include:

 1. Better resolution; therefore, less chance
 of interferences in the SIM quantitation.

2.   Sharper peaks; therefore better sensitivity.

3.   The ability to operate at lower temperatures
     with less chance of loss of sample due to
     adsorption and thermal decomposition.

Figure 5 compares chromatograms of Δ^8- and Δ^9-
THC-TMS and 11-hydroxy-Δ^8-THC-TMS obtained on a glass
capillary column and a 6ft. x 2mm I.D. packed column.
The retention times of the cannabinoids are comparable,
but the resolution and sensitivity achieved on the
capillary column is far superior. The capacity of the
capillary column is of course far less than that of the
packed column. Nevertheless, by using a Grob-type
splitless injector (7) we are able to inject several
microliters of solution containing up to 50 ng of each
cannabinoid without overloading the column. Use of
a support-coated open tubular column should increase
the column capacity, but at some sacrifice of resolution and sensitivity.

*Quantitation Using CI Mass Spectrometry and
Selected Ion Monitoring.*

Measurement of the ratio of concentrations of
each cannabinoid and its deuterated analog is achieved
using chemical ionization and the technique of selected ion monitoring as previously described. Because
of the low carrier gas flow rate used for capillary
columns, we can use virtually any carrier gas we want
(helium, hydrogen, etc.) and simply introduce our reagent gas or gases into the ion course via the make-up
gas inlet.

Figure 6 shows the methane-ammonia CI mass spectrum of the bis-trimethylsilyl derivative of 11-nor
Δ^9-THC carboxylic acid. As in the methane-ammonia
CI mass spectra of the other cannabinoids, the only
abundant ion corresponds to the protonated molecule
ion (MH^+). The computer program we use to control the
mass spectrometer during selected ion monitoring permits monitoring of different sets of ion masses for
specific intervals during the GC/MS analysis. Therefore, to measure all three cannabinoids during a single run we can monitor m/e 387 and 390 corresponding
to the MH^+ of d_0- and d_3-Δ^9-THC-TMS until they have
eluted, then switch to monitoring m/e 475 and 478, and
finally m/e 489 and 492, corresponding to the protonated molecule ions of d_0-and d_3-11-hydroxy-Δ^9-THC
TMS and d_0- and d_3-11-nor Δ^9-THC-9-carboxylic acid TMS,

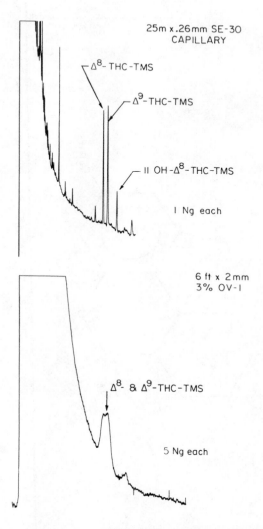

Figure 5. Comparison of capillary and packed column performances

respectively. In this way we can maximize the amount
of time spent integrating the ion current of each compound of interest while it is eluting from the GC column.

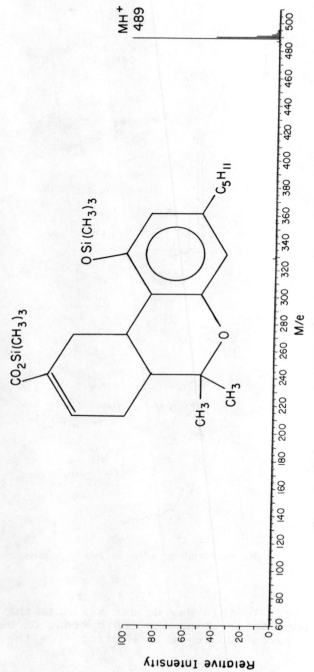

Figure 6.   Methane–ammonia CI–MS of 11-nor-Δ⁹-THC-9-carboxy TMS derivative

III.   CONCLUSIONS

The method we are using for quantitation of Δ^9-THC in blood, involving solvent extraction and GC/MS quantitation, has been used in our laboratory for over 1 year. It gives satisfactory results for THC concentrations down to 0.5 ng/ml if at least 0.5 ml of plasma, is available.

Our HPLC/capillary/GC CI-MS method for simultaneous measurement of THC and several of its metabolites appears very promising, but has not been fully reduced to practice. It may seem that employing such an array of high performance and expensive techniques for this type of analysis is "instrumental over-kill." However, we believe that it will prove very useful in our situation, because of its potential for high sensitivity, wide versatility, and extensive automation.

ACKNOWLEDGEMENT

This work was supported by the National Institute on Drug Abuse, Contracts ADM-45-74-140 and HSM-42-72-183.

REFERENCES

(1)   Agurell, S., Gustafsson, B., Holmstedt, B., Leander, K., Lindgren, J. E., Nilsson, I., Sandberg, F., and Asberg, M., *J. Pharm. Pharmac.* *25*, 554 (1973).

(2)   Wall, M. E., Harvey, T. M., Bursey, J. T., Brine, P. R., and Rosenthall, D., "Cannabinoid Assays in Humans", NIDA Research Monograph No. 7, Rockville, Maryland, 1976, p. 107.

(3)   Detrick, R., and Foltz, R. L., "Cannabinoid Assays in Humans", NIDA Research Monograph No. 7, Rockville, Maryland, 1976, p. 88.

(4)   Foltz, R. L., Knowlton, D. A., Lin, D. L. K., and Fentiman, Jr., A. F., Proceedings of the Second International Conference on Stable Isotopes, Oct. 20-23, 1975, Argonne, Illinois, p. 536.

(5)   Fenimore, D. L., Davis, C. M., Whitford, J. H. and Harrington, C. A., *Anal. Chem. 48*, 2289 (1976).

(6)   Graffeo, A. P., Lin, D. C. K., and Foltz, R. L. *J. Chromatogr.* *126*, 717 (1976).

(7)   Grob, K., and Grob, G., *Chromatographia* *5*, 3 (1972).

RECEIVED December 12, 1978.

Improvement of the Mass Fragmentographic Technique for Quantification of Tetrahydrocannabinol in Human Blood Plasma

AGNETA OHLSSON and STIG AGURELL—Department of Pharmacognosy, Faculty of Pharmacy, BMC, Box 579, S-751 23 Uppsala, Sweden

JAN-ERIK LINDGREN—Astra Lakemedel AB, S-151 85 Sodertalje, Sweden

KURT LEANDER—Department of Organic Chemistry, Arrhenius-laboratoriet, University of Stockholm, Fack, S-104 05 Stockholm, Sweden

In 1973 we investigated a mass fragmentographic method to determine Δ^1-tetrahydrocannabinol (THC) in plasma from cannabinis smokers (1,2). This method was used for pharmacokinetic studies of Δ^6-THC in man after smoking, where the plasma levels were correlated with physiological and psychological effects (3). To improve the sensitivity and to give an alternative route if interfering endogenous lipids or other contaminants appear, we have now developed a derivatization procedure for the determination of Δ^1-THC and Δ^6-THC by this nanogram-sensitive technique.

METHODS

The synthetic procedures for deuterium labelled THC used to have been published elsewhere (4,5). d_2-Labelled Δ^1- and Δ^6-THC were synthesized starting from 3,5-dimethoxybenzoic acid. The content of unlabelled THC in the final product was determined from mass spectroscopy to be 10%. To increase the number of deuterium atoms in the molecule and to obtain a lower content of unlabelled THC we therefore, with some modifications, used the method of Pitt et al, (6). For the synthesis of d_3- or d_7-labelled THC 5-(3,5-dimeth-

oxy-phenyl)-penta-2,4-dienoate was used as starting
material. The deuterium content was for the d_3-ana-
logue (m/e 314, 317) : d_0 0.7%, d_3 100% and for the
d_7-analogue (m/e 314, 321) : d_0 2%, d_7 100%. The compounds were found to be more than 95% pure according to
GLC. The positions of the deuterium in Δ^1-THC and
Δ^1-THC and Δ^6-THC are shown in Fig. 1.

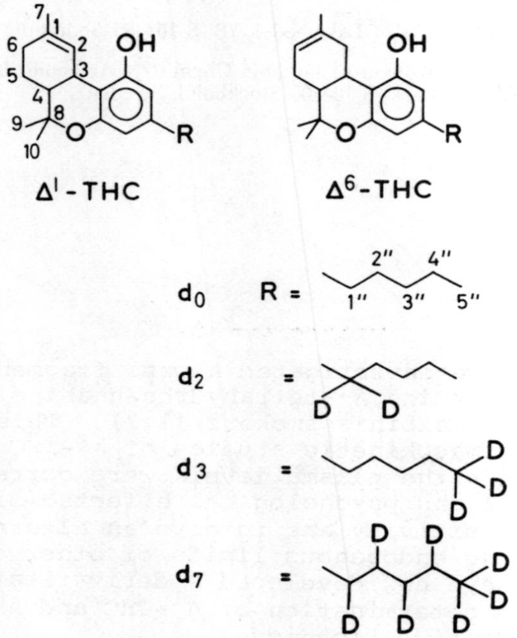

Figure 1. Formulas of Δ^1-THC and Δ^6-THC and deuterium containing internal
standards

ANALYSIS OF THC IN BLOOD PLASMA

The following procedure was used for Δ^1-THC (1,2)
and for Δ^6-THC (3). In addition a silylation step was
introduced.

BLOOD SAMPLES

Plasma samples were obtained from subjects after smoking cannabis samples containing 5-20 mg Δ^1-THC or Δ^6-THC. In another test, subjects were given oral doses of up to 50 mg Δ^1-THC. Blood samples (10 ml) from smokers were collected as needed in heparinized tubes. Plasma (5 ml) obtained by centrifugation was stored in silanized glass tubes at -20°C until analysis. The plasma samples (1-4 ml) obtained from subjects given oral doses of Δ^1-THC were frozen after centrifugation and stored at -20°C for four months before analysis.

EXTRACTION

To a 1-4 ml plasma sample is added 10 ng of deuterated internal standard (Δ^1-THC-d$_3$) dissolved in 50 µl ethanol. The extraction procedure and the liquid chromatographic purification on Sephadex LH-20 columns are described in detail in our previous studies (1-3). The purified sample was dissolved in absolute ethanol (10 µl) and kept cold (-20°C) and dark until analysis. This solution can be subjected to mass fragmentography directly or after silylation.

SILYLATION

On the day of analysis the samples were dried under nitrogen and dissolved in 25 µl dry acetonitrile, mixed with 10 µl silylating agent BSA--N,O,bis-tri-methylsilyl)-acetamide--or BSTFA--N,O-bis-(trimethyl-silyl)-triflouroacetamide--and kept at 50-60° for 10 minutes. The solutions were evaporated to dryness under a stream of nitrogen and redissolved in 10 µl dry acetonitrile and 2 µl was subjected to mass fragmentography.

MASS FRAGMENTOGRAPHY

Mass fragmentography was carried out using an LKB 2091 GC-MS instrument. The column was a 1.4x2mm i.d. silanized glass column containing 3% OV-17 or 3% SE-30 on Gas Chrom Q 100/120 mesh. Temperatures were in the column 210°C, flash heater 250°C and ion source 290°C. Helium was carrier gas (25 ml/min) and typical retention times were: Δ^6-THC 4.0 min. and Δ^1-THC 4.5 min. Lower column temperatures (180°C) was used for the silylated cannabinoids. For mass fragmentography a multiple ion detector was added (7). For Δ^1-THC-TMS

(TMS=trimethylsilyl) the mass spectrometer was set to
continuously record the intensity of m/e 386 (molecular
ion) and for the internal standard Δ^1-THC-d_3-TMS the
intensity of m/e 389 (molecular ion). The ionizing
potential was optimized at 50 eV for both the silylated
and underivatized THC.

The relative standard deviation when 1 ng was in-
je-ted was 2.7% (n=5) and with 0.5 ng injected 5.7%
(n=5).

The standard curves were prepared by adding known
amount of Δ^1-THC (0.5 - 20 ng/ml) to blank plasma samples and carrying out the described procedure (Fig. 2).
The correctness of the standard curves was checked during the day.

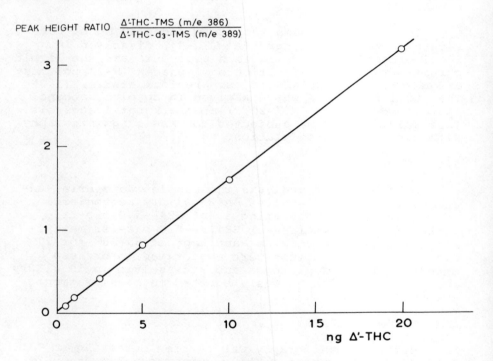

Figure 2.   Standard curve for Δ^1-THC-TMS (0–20 ng/mL) in plasma

RESULTS AND DISCUSSION

The extraction procedure for both Δ^1-THC and Δ^6-
THC, as revealed by experiment with tritium labelled

compounds is quite efficient and the recovery after
both extraction and liquid chromatographic purification
is usually over 80%. The pertinent fraction 5 ml from
the Sephadex LH-20 column contains over 90% of the peak,
but a 7-8 ml fraction is collected. The sensitivity in
the final mass fragmentographic assay may be limited by
the amount of non-labelled (d_0) compound present in the
deuterated internal standard. This interferes with the
non-labelled THC in the plasma. Thus, we have tried to
minimize this interference by increasing the number of
hydrogens substituted with deuterium, and by limiting
the amount of internal standard in the samples containing low amounts of THC. Thus, the present limit of
sensitivity is partly due to the amount of THC-d_0 in
the internal standard and not due to the chromatographic
or mass spectrometric problems per se. As expected,
d_3-containing THC showed, together with Δ^1-THC-d_7, the
least contamination with d_0-analogues (0.7-2%).

The present sensitivity for underivatized THC is
0.3 ng/ml plasma. This sensitivity is still not satisfactory to follow Δ^1-THC levels in plasma from subjects,
more than 12-24 hours. In order to improve the sensitivity it may also be necessary to reduce the blood
sample volumes or to eliminate compounds interfering
with mass fragmentography. After silylation, the sensitivity increased down to 0.1 ng/ml plasma. With a
sensitivity of 0.1 ng/ml plasma it may perhaps be possible to establish a true elimination phase for Δ^1-THC
in man. Lemberger and co-workers (8) have estimated
elimination phase half-lives in man of 1-2 days.

Typical mass fragmentograms from the determinations
of Δ^1-THC levels in man after oral administration are
shown in Fig. 3. The plasma level of 0.2 ng/ml was
determined from a total volume of 2.25 ml plasma.

We have so far encountered little interference in
the mass fragmentographic determination of THC provided redistilled solvents, particularly ethanol, and
all glass apparatus are used. If interference does
occur, the silylation technique provides an alternative.

This method can also be used to determine both underivatized or silylated cannabidiol and cannabinol
from plasma.

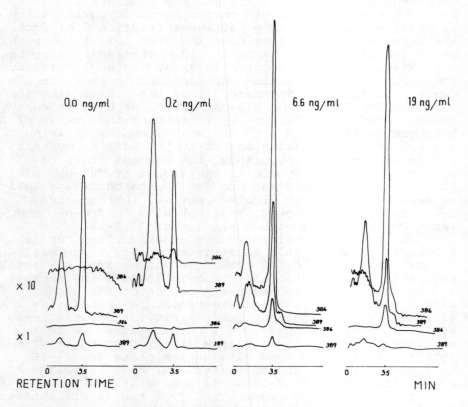

Figure 3. Mass fragmentograms of Δ^1-THC-TMS (m/e 386) with Δ^6-THC-d_3-TMS as internal standard (m/e 389) from purified plasma extracts. Plasma levels of 0.0, 0.2, 6.6, and 19 ng/mL.

ACKNOWLEDGMENTS

The support of the Swedish Medical Research Council is appreciated. A.O. wishes to express her gratitude to the Apotekarsocieteten for awarding a scholarship.

REFERENCES

(1)   Agurell, S., Gustafsson, B., Holmstedt, B., Leander, K., Lindgren, J-E., Nilsson, I., Sandberg, F., and Asberg, M., *J. Pharm. Pharmac.* 25, 554 (1973).

(2)   Agurell, S., "The Poisoned Patient: The Role of
        the Laboratory", Ciba Roundation Symposium 26,
        Elsevier-Excerpt Medica-North-Holland, Amsterdam-
        Oxford-New York, 1974, p. 125.
(3)   Agurell, S., Levander, S., Binder, M., Bader-
        Barfai, A., Gustafsson, B., Leander, K.,
        Lindgren, J-E., Ohlsson, A., and Tobisson, B.,
        in "Pharmacology of Cannabis", Eds. S. Szara
        and M. Braude, Raven Press, New York, 1974.
(4)   Ohlsson, A., Lindgren, J-E., Leander, K.,
        Agurell, S., "Cannabinoid Assays in Humans,
        NIDA Research Monograph Series, No. 7, 1976.
(5)   Ohlsson, A., Lindgren, J-E., Leander, K.,
        Agurell, S., in "Mass Spectroscopy in Drug Meta-
        bolism", Eds. A. Frigerio and E. Chisalberti,
        Plenum Press, New York, 1976.
(6)   Pitt, C. G., Hobbs, D. T., Schran, H., Twine
        Jr., C. E. and Williams, D. L., *J. Label. Comp.*
        11, 551 (1975).
(7)   Elkin, K., Pierrou, L., Ahlborg, U. G.,
        Holmstedt, B., Lindgren, J-E., *J. Chromatogr. 81*,
        47 (1973).
(8)   Lemberger, L., Axelrod, J., and Kopin, I. J.,
        New York Acad. Sci. 191, 142 (1971).

RECEIVED December 12, 1978.

A General Approach to the Analysis of Cannabinoids from Physiological Sources

J. ROSENFELD

Department of Pathology, McMaster Medical Centre, Hamilton, Ontario, Canada

It has been established that after smoking a pharmacological dose of Δ^9-THC the plasma concentrations of that drug do not rise above several hundred ng/ml of plasma and that during the period of psychological effect the concentration is less than 50 ng/ml. Since Δ^9-THC and many of its metabolites are lipophilic, the general problem is summarized as the determination of nanogram quantities of a lipophilic drug in the lipid fraction of plasma.

Determination of concentration in the ng/ml range requires the highly sensitive detectors of gas chromatography, such as electron capture (EC), alkali flame (AF), and mass spectrometry (MS). The situation, however, is complicated by the lipophiles present in the plasma and/or serum. This problem was highlighted when EC was used to achieve the required sensitivity. Fenimore (1) and Garrett (2) reported on EC methods for Δ^9-THC in human serum and dog plasma, respectively. Both used acylation with highly fluorinated reagents to prepare derivatives for EC detection. However, there was a dramatic change in the gas chromatographic traces and apparent interferences from lipophiles. The cause for the differences has not been determined but these results prompted Mechoulam to warn that in the analysis of Δ^9-THC and its metabolites it may not be possible to simply exchange plasma of different species but that each may, in fact, be different (3).

When the problem is expanded to include the determination of metabolites the situation becomes more complex (Fig. 1).

0-8412-0488-8/79/47-098-081$05.00/0

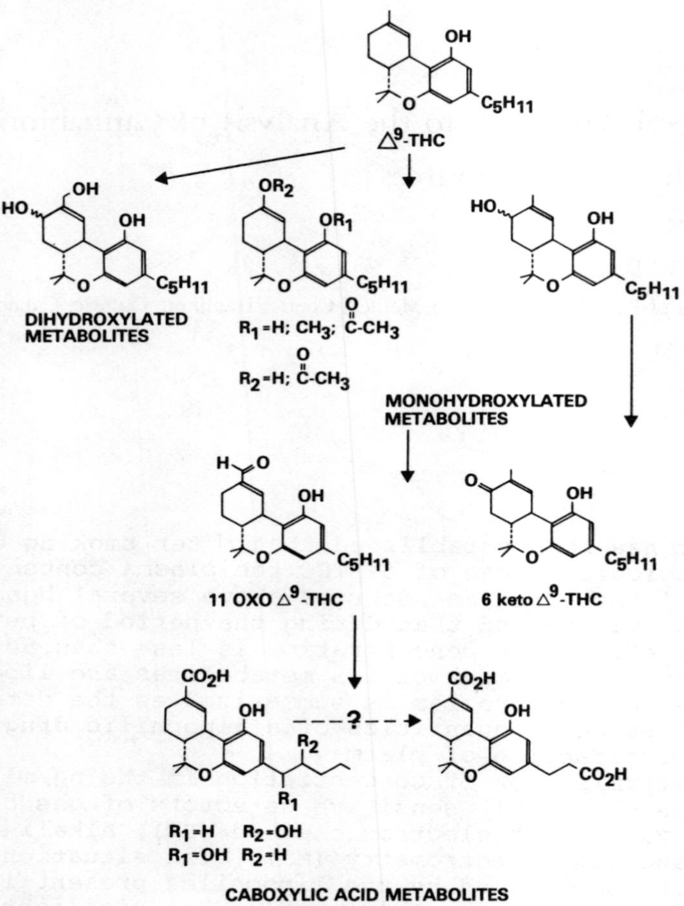

Figure 1.   Metabolism of Δ⁹-THC

When we first approached the study on the determination of the cannabinoids by mass spectrometry, we were somewhat intimidated by the large number of possible metabolites. We were also concerned about the requirement of deuterated analogs of the compounds for mass spectrometric determination. The difficulties involved in the synthesis of nonlabeled compounds, however, argued for an approach that did not require total synthesis of the deuterated analogs.

We therefore applied Occham's razor to our deliberations and decided that, in fact, with only one

or two exceptions, we were dealing with phenols. The
problem then "reduced" to the analysis of lipid soluble phenols in the lipid matrix of plasma.

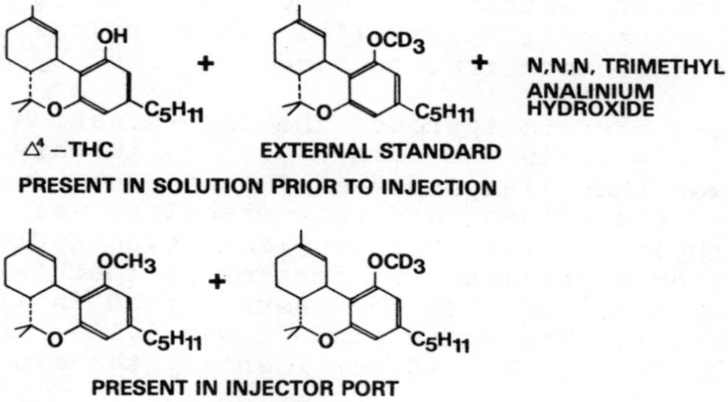

Δ⁴-THC   **EXTERNAL STANDARD**

PRESENT IN SOLUTION PRIOR TO INJECTION

PRESENT IN INJECTOR PORT

Figure 2.   Derivatization of THC

      Our original method for Δ^9-THC explored this
problem to some extent. Rather than attempt the synthesis of deutero labeled Δ^9-THC we decided to analyze
Δ^9-THC as its own methyl ether (Fig. 2). Our internal
standard would be 1-O-perdeuteriomethyl-Δ^9-THC. It
was proposed to convert Δ^9-THC to its 1-O-methyl ether
for the analysis. This was effected by the co-inject-
ion of trimethylanilinium hydroxide and Δ^9-THC. At
the elevated temperatures of the injector port the
phenol is converted to its methyl derivative. This
conversion is both reproducible and quantitative. It
is therefore suitable for use in any analytical technique.
      The problem of lipophiles remained and here again
we could make use of the acid functionality of the
phenols. With less lipid soluble phenols such as the
steroids, simple back extraction from organic solvent
into strong base would have been sufficient. However,
the high lipid solubility of Δ^9-THC necessitated that
extraction be carried out with Brodie's solvent (hexane and isoamyl alcohol) and that back extraction be
done with Claisen's alkali, which is a mixture of KOH,
methanol, and water. After acidification of the
Claisen's alkali, Δ^9-THC could be recovered by extraction. The external standard and the trimethylanilinium
hydroxide were added and the extracted phenol (i.e.
Δ^9-THC) was converted to the 1-O-methyl derivative
in the injector port and the determination carried out

by mass spectrometry.

Using this method we were able to obtain plasma concentration profiles from humans who had smoked cigarettes dosed at 88 µg THC/kg. Thirty minutes after smoking; the concentration ranged from 5 to 35 ng/ml with an average of 17 ng/ml (4). These values were similar to the concentration range reported by Agurell (5).

We attempted to approach the determination of 11-hydroxy-Δ^9-THC in the same way. Preliminary experiments showed that 11-hydroxy-Δ^9-THC was not very soluble in Brodie's solvent and the metabolite was unstable to methylation with trimethylanilinium hydroxide. In the latter experiment, we determined that two products were formed, but they were formed in irreproducible ratios. The major product was 1,11,-dimethyl-11-hydroxy-Δ^9-THC. We did not identify the minor product.

It was clear that a milder form of derivatization was required if we were to be successful in carrying on with our original philosophy of analyzing the cannabinoids as their 1-0-alkyl derivatives. We found that the technique of phase transfer catalysis suited our requirements.

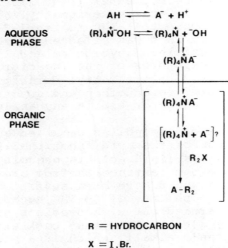

Figure 3. Phase transfer alkylation process

This technique involves the extraction of the anion of an organic acid as its ion pair with a lipid soluble quaternary ammonium cation (in our case, this

was tetrahexyl ammonium hydroxide); if the organic
phase contains an alkylating agent such as a bromo or
iodo hydrocarbon the anion becomes alkylated as in
Fig. 3. The exact mechanism involved in this alkylation is still uncertain. Whatever the actual mechanism both methyl and ethyl iodide were equally reactive,
giving the 1-O-alkyl derivative in quantitative yield.
This was important because the 1-O-methyl ether of
11-hydroxy-Δ^9-THC has been shown to be a metabolite of
11-hydroxy-Δ^9-THC (6). Thus by derivatizing to the
ethyl ether we were certain that we would be specifically measuring 11-hydroxy-Δ^9-THC and not an endoge-
nously formed metabolite (Fig. 4).

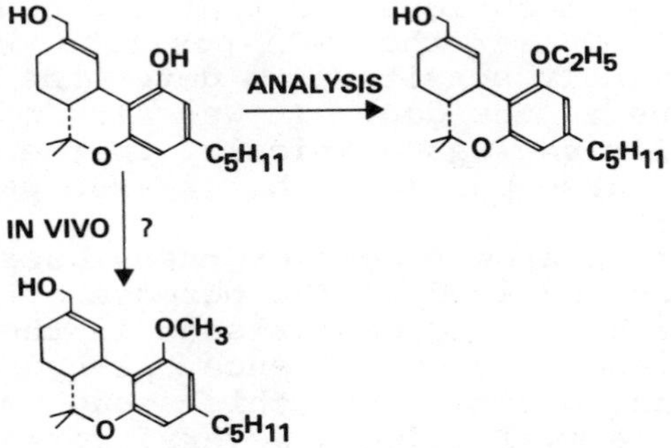

Figure 4.   Analysis and metabolism of 11-hydroxy-Δ^9-THC

There was one further problem, namely the 1-O-
ethyl-11-hydroxy-Δ^9-THC was susceptible to pyrolysis
at the elevated temperatures of the ion source. This
resulted in irreproducible mass spectra. Silylation
of the allylic alcohol functionality overcame this
difficulty and the resulting electron impact fragmentation pattern was quite simple showing only one major
peak, base peak at m/e = 327. The trimethylsilyl ion
appeared at m/e = 73   (7).
This was interesting because there are several
monohydroxylic metabolites of Δ^9-THC. If we were
monitoring, say, the molecular ion, we would detect
all of these metabolites. Since 327 results from a
loss of C-11, this ion is specific for the derivative
of 11-hydroxy-Δ^9-THC. This is probably a minor point,
because the various monohydroxylated metabolites have
been shown to be separable by gas chromatography.
Nevertheless, it does result in a highly specific determination for the most debated metabolite.
Due to the specificity of the mass spectrometer
the problem of lipophiles was not limiting in the

determination of the hydroxy metabolite. Simple extraction with methylene chloride gave an extract sufficiently clean to permit, after appropriate derivatization, determination of concentrations of several nanograms per milliliter.

We carried out a study in the dog to determine the formation of 11-hydroxy-Δ^9-THC from Δ^9-THC. In the first stage we injected 11-hydroxy-Δ^9-THC in order to determine the beta phase half-life of the metabolite; the half-life was approximately 1.5 hours. However, when Δ^9-THC was administered to the same dog either orally or intravenously the metabolite was not detectable.

There are several possible explanations for this result. The most obvious are that the dog does not hydroxylate Δ^9-THC at the C-11 position or our method was insufficiently sensitive to determine the very low concentrations in the dog. It was also possible that this particular dog was atypical. In the case of oral dosage it was also possible that Δ^9-THC was not readily absorbed.

In order to answer some of these questions we embarked on a second study. The purpose of this study was to show that Δ^9-THC was present in the circulation of an animal and as a consequence, 11-hydroxy-Δ^9-THC appeared in the plasma. For this study we chose the rabbit as our animal model. Several workers have shown that the rabbit oxidizes Δ^9-THC at the C-11 position and also that rabbit liver microsomes oxidize Δ^9-THC at the C-11 position and also that rabbit liver microsomes oxidize Δ^9-THC to 11-hydroxy-Δ^9-THC. We were thus assured that we would not be dealing with a species where there was doubt about oxidation at C-11 (3).

Before entering into the study we felt that it would be useful to have a method that would determine both parent drug and metabolite simultaneously. There were two reasons for this; first, the logistics of the work would be greatly improved since only one determination would have to be carried out per sample of plasma; second, our original hypothesis was that, by exploitation of the chemistry of the phenol groups we could determine Δ^9-THC and most of its metabolites. Our first two techniques determined these compounds but by different extraction and derivatizations. Therefore, these techniques lacked general applicability to the cannabinoids. Our philosophy held true but our chemistry did not.

A simple study on the simultaneous extraction of radio-labeled Δ^9-THC and 11-hydroxy-Δ^9-THC once again

showed that anything alive or even something once
associated with a living entity can and usually does
throw a curve at the analytical chemist. When Δ^9-THC
was extracted from water, methylene chloride and diethyl ether extracted the drug quantitatively whereas
toluene extracted only 80% of the Δ^9-THC. However,
when extractions were carried out from human plasma or
rabbit plasma both methylene chloride and ethyl ether
extracted less than 45% of the compounds. Toluene,
however, still extracted approximately 80% in both
cases. In addition the yield of extraction from rabbit
plasma was slightly higher than that found in human
plasma. There are three things that are striking
about these data. First, despite the acknowledged
lipid solubility of Δ^9-THC, the drug, as documented by
Garrett and Hunt, is to some extent, soluble in water
(7). Consequently, it is not completely extractable
in all organic solvents. In fact, only the polar
solvents such as diethyl ether and methylene chloride
are capable of quantitatively extracting Δ^9-THC from
water. Second, it is surprising that those solvents
that extract Δ^9-THC efficiently from water are not
efficient at extracting it from plasma. It is also
interesting that there is no change in the extraction
efficiency using toluene. Finally it is interesting
that the extraction efficiency for all three solvents
is slightly higher from rabbit plasma than from human
plasma.

It is not possible, currently, to offer an explanation for these observations, but perhaps it is per-
missible to speculate. The low efficiency with methylene chloride might be explained by the fact that proteins precipitate when plasma is extracted with this
solvent. Since Δ^9-THC is bound to protein, it may
co-precipitate and not be extracted from precipitate.
However, co-precipitation with proteins cannot be
invoked to explain the results with diethyl ether
since this solvent does not cause protein precipitation. Furthermore, it is also necessary to explain
the observation on extraction with toluene and the
differences between rabbit and human plasma. The co-
precipitation argument is simply not applicable to
these phenomena.

We hypothesize that a subtle drug protein inter-
action occurs when polar solvents are used to extract
highly lipid soluble drugs from plasma. These solvents are capable of delipidizing lipoproteins. It is
possible that, when delipidization occurs, the hydrophobic region of that protein is exposed. The hydrophobic region could then bind Δ^9-THC and the binding

forces might be sufficiently great that they interfere
with the extraction into organic solvent. Since
toluene is not as efficient a solvent for lipid extraction, it is possible that this solvent does not
delipidize the lipoproteins to the same extent as the
more polar solvents. Consequently the extraction
efficiency with toluene is relatively unchanged. We
did not have sufficient radio-labeled 11-hydroxy-Δ^9-
THC to carry out as exhaustive a study with that compound. Worst case analysis showed that the extraction
efficiency of this compound from human plasma was
quite high. The phenomena therefore may be limited
to Δ^9-THC and possibly to other drugs with relatively
high lipid solubility.

The delipidization hypothesis is attractive because it can also explain the difference between the
extraction efficiency from rabbit and human plasma.
A major difference between human and rabbit plasma is
that the latter has less and possibly different lipoproteins. If the hypothesis that lipoproteins affect
the extraction efficiency for Δ^9-THC is correct, this
could explain the somewhat higher extraction efficiencies from plasma. These results support Mechoulam's
argument that, in the analysis of Δ^9-THC in plasma,
it may be necessary to consider the biological source
of the plasma (3).

These observations define one of the problems in
external calibration methods for the analysis of Δ^9-
THC. However, when this difficulty is recognized and
accounted for, external calibration becomes a plausible technique.

Having determined the most appropriate extraction
from plasma we investigated the simultaneous derivatization of Δ^9-THC and 11-hydroxy-Δ^9-THC. We have
claimed that ethylation of 11-hydroxy-Δ^9-THC proceeded
by phase transfer catalysis (7). However, it is known
that quaternary ammonium hydroxides are capable of
catalyzing alkylations with alkyl iodides in aprotic
solvents (8). Furthermore, we had not demonstrated
that Δ^9-THC could be derivatized under the same conditions as 11-hydroxy-Δ^9-THC. We found that the minimum
requirement for the reaction to proceed is the presence of water, which probably increases the degree
of ionization of the quaternary ammonium hydroxide.
However, in order for the reaction to go to completion,
at least 0.1N NaOH is necessary. This supports the
contention that this derivatization is, to some extent, a phase transfer catalyzed alkylation.

Ethylation of Δ^9-THC proved to be fortuitous.
The base peak in the mass spectrum of this compound is
also m/e = 327. This was important to us because we

had a dual ion detection instrument and it was fortunate that both parent drug and metabolite, when derivatized, generated the same peak. However, the fragmentation of 1-O-ethyl-Δ^9-THC was more extensive than
that of the metabolites. Consequently, the sensitivity to Δ^9-THC determination on our instrument was decreased.

   At this stage we also investigated the formation
of derivatives that would permit analysis by gas
chromatographic techniques other than gas chromatogra-
phy/mass spectrometry. We first investigated the reaction with pentafluorobenzyl bromide (PFBB). We found
that PFBB is as reactive as the simple alkyl iodides
(Fig. 5) consequently the pentafluorobenzyl derivatives
of THC are readily prepared.

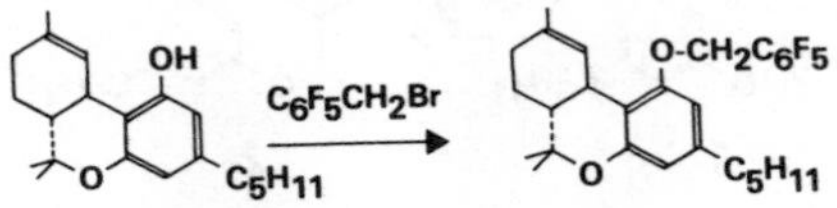

NORMALITY NaOH	RATIO 2/1
0.01	>100
0.1	>100
1	>100
5	>100
10	>100

*Figure 5.   Conditions for the alkylation of Δ^9-THC with pentafluorobenzyl bro-
mide*

   We chose this derivative because we wanted to apply it to electron capture determination and possibly
high pressure liquid chromatography determinations
(HPLC). A review of the literature suggested that,
while PFB derivatives are detectable at the picogram
level by EC detection, PFBB is difficult to remove and
can cause interferences with the determinations. We
therefore also investigated derivatization with trifluoroethyl iodide a reagent with a low boiling point
(58°C). This reagent was less reactive than the alkyl
or benzyl halides as seen in (Fig. 6). This is probably due to the electron withdrawing properties of the
three flourine atoms, resulting in a stronger carbon
iodine bond. Nevertheless, under proper conditions,
it is possible to obtain a high degree of derivatization. It appears, therefore, that the phase transfer
catalyzed alkylation can be applicable to the development of EC and possibly HPLC as well as mass spectrometric methods. For the present, however, we limited

our studies to the GC/MS technique.

We had shown that it was possible to extract both
Δ^9-THC and 11-hydroxy-Δ^9-THC from plasma with toluene.
The next question was the problem of lipophiles. Again
we found that in order to remove interferences to Δ^9-
THC determinations it was necessary to fractionate the
toluene extract with Claisen's alkali in order to obtain the phenol fraction of plasma. We found that the
extractions of Δ^9-THC from toluene with Claisen's alkali is not quantitative, but it is reproducible. The
loss of Δ^9-THC in this reaction however, is compensated
for by removal of interferences which were the limiting factors in the single extraction step.

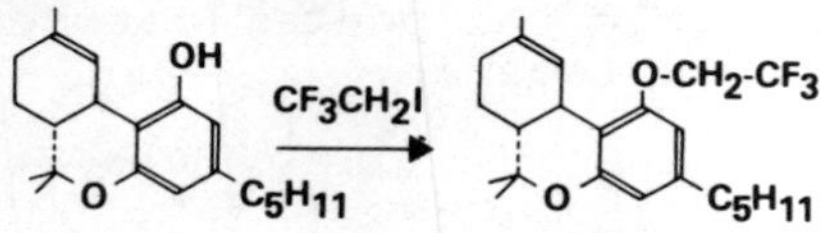

1	2
NORMALITY NaOH	RATIO 2/1
0.01	0.06
0.1	0.65
1N	2.9
5N	10
10N	18

Figure 6.   Conditions for the derivatization of Δ^9-THC with trifluoroethyl iodide

The final analytical method for the simultaneous
determination of Δ^9-THC and its metabolites consists
of the following sequence: the cannabinoids are extracted from plasma with toluene; they are then back
extracted from toluene into Claisen's alkali; the
Claisen's alkali is diluted with water, tetrahexyl
ammonium hydroxide is added and the alkaline solution
is extracted with methylene chloride containing ethyl
iodide. The overall recoveries were 45% for Δ^9-THC
and 83% for 11-hydroxy-Δ^9-THC. External standards
(1-O-ethyl-Δ^9-THC and 1-O-ethyl-11-hydroxy-Δ^9-THC)
were added to the methylene chloride phase followed by
a small amount of Florosil, which absorbed the tetrahexylammonium hydroxide and tetrahexylammonium iodide.
The methylene chloride was decanted and evaporated.
The residue was taken up in a mixture of N,O-bis-(trimethylsilyl)-acetamide and trimethylchlorosilane (9/1).
The final solution was used for GC/MS analysis.

This technique was used to investigate the appearance of 11-hydroxy-Δ^9-THC in the plasma of rabbits that

had been dosed with Δ^9-THC. The rabbits received
100 μg/kg, which was slightly higher than that used in
the human study. 11-hydroxy-Δ^9-THC was present in the
circulation within 5 minutes at a concentration of 10
ng/ml and rapidly declined so that at 45 minutes there
were no detectable concentrations. These data do not
deny or confirm the hypothesis that 11-hydroxy-Δ^9-THC
is an active metabolite. They do, however suggest a
type of experiment that is possible when methods of
determination are available. If we take the argument
that we administered a pharmacologically active dose to
the rabbit then it is clear that if 11-hydroxy-Δ^9-THC
is to be considered an active metabolite it must be
shown to be active at concentrations less than 10 ng/ml.

REFERENCES

(1) Fenimore, D. C., Freeman, R. R., and Loy, P. R.,
    Anal. Chem. 45, 2331 (1973).
(2) Garrett, E. R., and Hunt, C. A., *J. Pharm. Sci.
    62*, 1211 (1973).
(3) Mechoulam, R., McCallum, N. K., and Burstein, S.,
    Chem. Revs. 76, 75 (1976).
(4) Rosenfeld, J., Bowins, B., Roberts J., Perkins, J.,
    and Macpherson, A. S., *Anal. Chem. 46*, 2232 (1974)
(5) Agurell, S., Gustafsson, B., Holmstedt, B., Lean-
    der, K., Lindgren, J., Nilsson, I., Sandberg, F.,
    and Asberg, M., *J. Pharm. Pharmac. 25*, 554,
    (1973).
(6) Estevez, V. S., Englert, L. F., and Ho, B. T.,
    Res. Commun. Chem. Path. Pharm. 6, 821 (1973).
(7) Rosenfeld, J. M. and Taguchi, V. Y., *Anal. Chem.
    48*, 726 (1976).
(8) Fieser, L. F. and Fieser, M., "Reagents for Or-
    ganic Synthesis", John Wiley and Sons, New York,
    1967, p. 1252.

RECEIVED December 12, 1978.

Quantitation of Δ⁹-Tetrahydrocannabinol and Its Metabolites in Human Urine by Probability Based Matching GC/MS

DONALD E. GREEN, FU-CHUAN CHAO, KAY O. LOEFFLER, and SAUL L. KANTER

Veterans Administration Hospital, Palo Alto, CA 94304

Two independent research groups at our hospital have pursued the development of analytical methodology for THC and its metabolites in urine. One group, under L. E. Hollister, has directed its efforts primarily toward fractioning the in vivo THC metabolites by solvent partitioning and by TLC. The other group, under I. S. Forrest and D. E. Green, has been concerned with the development of an automated GC/MS quantitative procedure.

Five years ago both groups began using a multistep procedure for fractionating urinary THC metabolites according to their polarities and acidities utilizing manipulations of solvents and/or pH as seen in Figure 1 (1). This scheme can quantitatively extract all of the radioactivity from ^{14}C-THC-dosed Rhesus monkey urine, either hydrolyzed or unhydrolyzed. It separates the metabolic products derived from enzyme hydrolyzed specimens into one major fraction -- containing about half of the total quantity of metabolic material -- and four small, approximately equal, fractions. The fractions and the nature of the metabolites contained in each are: hexane extractable "non-polar neutrals" (designated as H); ether (pH 12) extractable "weakly polar neutrals" (designated as E-I); ether (pH 2.5) extractable "weakly polar acids" (designated as E-II and E-III); and ethyl acetate (pH 2.5) extractable "modera-

0-8412-0488-8/79/47-098-093$05.25/0

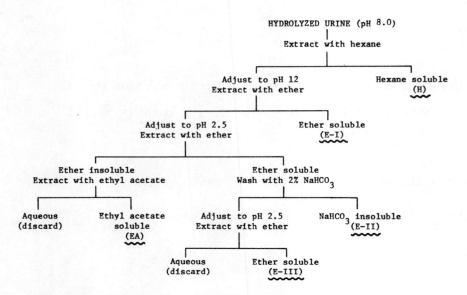

*Figure 1.   Extraction scheme used for β-glucuronidase/aryl sulfatase-hydrolyzed
Δ⁹-THC urines indicating derivation of the H, E-I, and E-II fractions*

tely polar acids" (designated as EA)   (2).   The remaining "highly polar" acidic metabolites can be extracted
with tetrahydrofuran at pH 2.5.   Figure 2 shows the
relationship between the sizes of these fractions in
hydrolyzed, as well as unhydrolyzed, urines.   Subsequently, this procedure was improved by resolving the
weakly polar acids, the largest single fraction, into
weak and strong acids (E-II and E-III, respectively --
in approximately a 1:5 ratio) according to their solubility in 2% NaHCO₃ solution.

Most of our work has been concentrated on the
three least polar fractions, H, E-I, and E-II, which
contain the parent cannabinoids and the neutral mono-
and di-hydroxys, as well as the "11-oic" acids.   We have
applied this fractionation scheme very extensively to
urines obtained from human volunteers following oral
administration of pure constituents of cannabis --
namely, Δ⁹-THC, CBN, CBD and 11-HO-Δ⁹-THC (singly and
in combinations).   These studies have revealed many
interesting phenomena which can be summarized briefly
as follows: 1)   the formation of a multitude of metabolites from each parent drug;   2)   very few of these
metabolites give TLC matches with available reference
compounds;   3)   the extreme persistence (at least 10
days) of polar acidic metabolites following a single

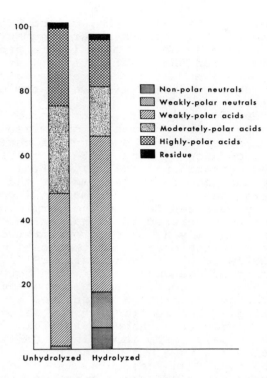

Non-polar neutrals
Weakly-polar neutrals
Weakly-polar acids
Moderately-polar acids
Highly-polar acids
Residue

Unhydrolyzed Hydrolyzed

Figure 2. Distribution according to polarity (extractability of Δ⁹-THC) of in vivo metabolites in hydrolyzed and unhydrolyzed Rhesus urine: nonpolar neutrals = extractable with hexane at natural pH; weakly polar neutrals = extractable with ether at pH 12; weakly polar acids = extractable with ether at pH 2; moderately polar acids = extractable with ethyl acetate at pH 2; highly polar acids = extractable with THF at pH 2.

administration of drug; and 4) the identification of Δ^9-THC-11-oic acid as a major acidic metabolite of Δ^9-THC. We have also established that semiquantitative comparisons of urine samples can be made if volumes containing equal quantities of creatinine are compared.

Quantitation of individual metabolites was obtained by a novel variation of GC/MS/COM data acquisition and processing (3) which uses an algorithm that was developed at Cornell University by Professor

F. E. McLafferty. This algorithm, called Probability
Based Matching or PBM, employs a large number of fragment ions in a reverse search mode (4) to provide reliable identification and quantitation of an individual,
specific compound even though the mass spectral measurements are derived from a mixture of two or more
compounds (5).

The degree of specificity of a reverse search identification is "tunable" and can be optimized by selection of unique ions from the spectrum of the target compound and by avoidance of ions that are characteristic
of anticipated contaminants that elute from the GC column at nearly the same retention time as the target
compound. Large sets of specific masses (typically 10
to 15 carefully selected ions in the format of a "contracted" spectrum) are used to characterize each compound, rather than relying on only one or two specific
ions as is usually the case in conventional mass fragmentography or selected ion monitoring (SIM). A statistical measure of the quality of match between the
experimental sample's contracted spectrum and the reference contracted spectrum is calculated by using a
unique weighting of the identity of the selected ions
and of their relative abundances (6). This matching
factor in the PBM algorithm is called a Confidence Index, or K-score, and is a binary logarithmic estimate
of the probability of an accidental match between an
unknown spectrum and a reference spectrum. A rough
approximation of the significance of K-scores is that
the spectra of 2^{Kth} compounds, chosen at random, would
have to be compared with the library spectrum in order
to find another set of data that match to the same degree as does the experimental spectrum. Thus a K of
10 (i.e. 2^{10}) means that approximately 1,000 randomly
selected spectra would have to be examined in order to
find another equally good fit. Obviously, the significance of this measurement increases very rapidly as K
gets larger -- e.g. for K = 20 there appears to be only
a "one in a million" chance that the experimentally derived contracted spectrum arises from a molecule un-
related to the target compound. As can be easily seen
in Figure 3, differential K-scores are of great qualitative usefulness; viz. one microgram of Δ^8-THC (when
used to challenge the set of ions chosen for the Δ^9-THC
assay program) gives a K-score of 14, more than 50
points lower than that produced by only 50 nanograms of
Δ^9-THC (the target compound) (7). Another way of des-
cribing this degree of specificity is that the "cross-
reactivity" between Δ^8-THC and the Δ^9-THC program, at
the μg level, is less than 1 part in 2^{102} (10^{30}).

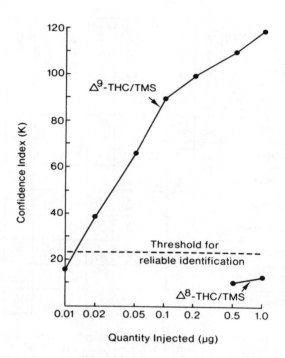

Figure 3. Effect produced on PBM Confidence Index by varying the quantity of pure Δ^9-THC injected (response to Δ^8-THC as a challenge)

The ability of our SIM assay programs to distinguish between closely related compounds can be seen in the matrix shown in Figure 4 (7). The Confidence Index (the upper number in each box) for each target compound is compared with that of the THC metabolites eluting from the column, immediately before it and after it (and therefore to most likely interfere with its assay). The lower number in each box is the retention time in seconds. In all cases, the difference in K-scores between the correct compound and its nearest neighbor is greater than 87 -- corresponding to a discrimination factor greater than 10^{27} (2^{87}).

The most unique and valuable feature of Probability Based Matching, when applied to biological extracts, is its ability to automatically detect the existence of contaminations in a GC peak and to eliminate their interferences. This unusual feat can be accomplished because PBM is a "self-adapting" SIM technique; i.e. the computer decides which ions in the contracted spectrum contain valid data and concurrently rejects ions that are contaminated due to the presence of impurities.

COMPOUND INTRODUCED \ COMPOUND MONITORED	DELTA-9-THC	CANNABINOL	8B-HO-D9-THC	11-HO-D9-THC	8A,11-DI-HO	8B,11-DI-HO	9-THC-11-OIC	CBN-11-OIC
DELTA-8-THC	14 / 81							
DELTA-9-THC	116 / 85	8 / 109						
CANNABINOL	10 / 85	144 / 111	7 / 121					
8B-HO-D9-THC		12 / 119	127 / 126	10 / 147				
11-HO-D9-THC			0 / 131	122 / 149	9 / 155			
8A,11-DI-HO				13 / 154	101 / 155	9 / 197		
8B,11-DI-HO					2 / 163	119 / 197	11 / 254	
9-THC-11-OIC						8 / 198	112 / 253	9 / 306
CBN-11-OIC							11 / 261	100 / 308

Figure 4. Confidence Indices (upper number) and retention times in sec (lower number) for 9 cannabinoids. Reported as K for 1 μg samples. (Column = 180 cm × 0.2 cm ID borosilicate glass packed with 1.5% OV-17 on 100/120 mesh HP Chromosorb G; column temperature = 275°C; nitrogen carrier flow rate = 30 mL/min)

Because of its central role in the performance of this instrument system, some of the unique aspects of PBM will be described in enough detail to permit an understanding of the operation of the algorithm. The mechanism by which self-adapting SIM is accomplished is as follows: first, the correct intensity ratios for the selected ions in the pure material are established by analyzing a reference standard; next the intensities of the selected ions in the unknown are measured, corrected for background, and compared with the reference values for the pure compound -- any ions that result from mixtures of the target compound and an impurity will be enhanced in magnitude and will cause uncontaminated ions to appear to be too weak in comparison; then, the absolute intensity of the pattern (that which represents the proper relative intensities of all of the selected ions) is allowed to decrease until it coincides with the single ion that represents the upper limit of the amount of the target compound. A tolerance is added to allow for variations in the experimental reproducibility of measurement of individual ions-- due to the fact that the ions are measured under dynamic conditions (e.g. a sharp GC peak) or to allow for instrumental instabilities -- and any ions that exceed the designated tolerance "window" are judged by the computer to be derived from mixtures of compounds and hence to not uniquely represent the target compound. These "contaminated" ions are ignored in the calculation of K-scores and in quantitation.

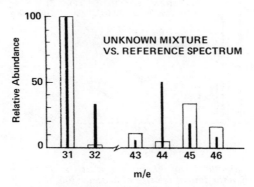

Figure 5. *Six-ion contracted spectrum of pure ethanol*

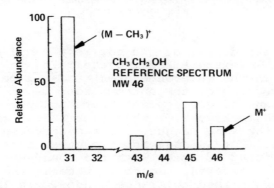

Figure 6. *Same six-ion contracted spectrum as Figure 5 for unknown mixture (solid lines) superimposed on ethanol spectrum (bars)*

PBM analysis may be clarified by a simple example. Figure 5 shows the values of m/e and the relative abundances found when a 6-ion contracted spectrum of pure ethanol is scanned. In Figure 6, the same contracted spectrum of an unknown mixture (solid vertical lines) has been measured, and is compared with the

ethanol reference spectrum. If the relative abundances
of the m/e 31 ions in the two spectra are made equal as
shown, the abundances of none of the other ions agree.
Ions such as m/e 32 and 44, which are too high in the
unknown spectrum, must be due to components other than
ethanol; the low abundances of the unknown at m/e 43,
45, and 46 shows that ethanol, if present, must exist
at a lower concentration than called for by the intensity of the ion at m/e 31.

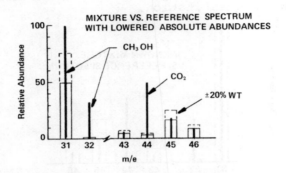

Figure 7. *Absolute abundances of ethanol contracted spectrum reduced so that
no ions are greater than the lowest relative abundance ion in contracted spectrum
of mixture. Contaminated ions are identified as those ions of the mixture that
exceed the relative intensities of the attenuated ethanol pattern (plus the prescribed window tolerance).*

If the abundances of the entire ethanol contracted
spectrum are lowered -- keeping their relative heights
the same as in the reference spectrum -- a point is
reached where none of the unknown ions is of lower
abundance than the corresponding ethanol peaks. In the
example shown in Figure 7, this occurs when the mass 46
ions become the same height. If a measurement reproducibility of ±20% is assumed, two other ions (m/e 43
and 45) are found to agree with the abundances required
by the ethanol reference spectrum because they fall
within the prescribed tolerance window. In this example, the mixture was about 50% ethanol; the excess intensities at m/e 31 and 32 were due to methanol and
the excess intensity at m/e 44 was due to the additional
presence of CO_2.

Thus, in the above example, there are three contaminated ions and three uncontaminated ions. Based
solely upon such uncontaminated ions in the contracted
spectrum of an experimental sample, PBM Confidence In-
Indices and quantitations are computed. The magnitude

of the K-score depends primarily upon the identities of, and the absolute number of, the <u>particular</u> ions which are judged to be uncontaminated. After three years of experience with this technique, we can say that a K-score greater than about 60 is virtual certainty of proper identification (especially when taken in conjunction with a correct GC retention time).

As one gains experience with these Confidence Indices, the practical significance of this statistical parameter becomes clearly manifest; for each and every determination, the likelihood that the data are valid is immediately apparent by inspection.

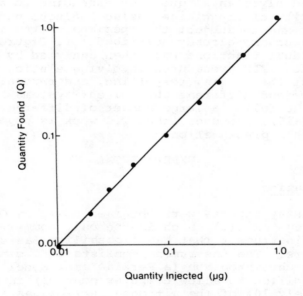

Figure 8. Quantitation reported by MS (PBM algorithm) as a function of the quantity of Δ⁹-THC actually injected into the GC

In PBM, Confidence Indices are automatically computed each time the set of selected ions is scanned -- which is several times each second -- and the single best fit, among all the scans of the experimental sample, is retained in the computer memory. Simultaneously the absolute intensity of each uncontaminated ion is compared with the absolute intensity of the corresponding ion (that was generated by a known quantity of the reference compound during the calibration procedure) to produce an independent "mass fragmentographic-type"

(SIM) quantitation for each uncontaminated ion. All of
these single ion quantitations are then averaged to provide a reliable estimate of the quantity of substance
present during each scan of the contracted spectrum.
The maximum quantity that is found is retained in memory and reported, along with the K-score and retention
time, at the end of the experiment. The quantitative
response of the PBM algorithm is linear for well over
two orders of magnitude (Figure 8).
    The major efforts of both of our groups have been
confined, to a large degree, to studying the time course
of individual THC metabolites in urine following oral
administration of pure THC. Our usual procedure has
been to hydrolyze an aliquot corresponding to a speci-
fied quantity of creatinine, using β-glucuronidase/aryl
sulfatase, and to subject the specimen to the multistep
extraction scheme already described (cf. Figure 1).
The individual fractions were then analyzed by TLC, GC/
MS, or HPLC. TLC procedures involving elution of the
region near the origin, respotting, and rerunning in
more polar (and different pH) solvent systems have permitted us to follow a large number of different metabolites (8-10). However, that TLC work is beyond the
scope of this presentation.

                        EXPERIMENTAL

Instrumentation

    The assay reports were obtained using an Olfax II
GC/MS/COM system[*] (3) which is the only commercially
available instrument that has Probability Based Matching software. The instrument consists of a conventional gas chromatograph (a Perkin-Elmer Model 3920
that is modified to allow computer control) in which
approximately 10% of the nitrogen carrier gas is led to
an FID and the remaining 90% is conducted via a heated,
glass lined, transfer line to a 2-stage silicone membrane separator that admits approximately half of the
sample, but only about 1 ppm of the carrier, into an
ion-pumped quadrupole mass spectrometer (UTI Model
100C) (11). A dedicated microcomputer controls or
monitors a variety of mass spectrometer parameters as
well as completely controls an automatic mode of operation -- including GC column temperature programming,
MS data acquisition which employs automatic adjustment

*Manufactured by Vitek Systems, Inc., a division of the
McDonnell Douglas Corporation, 430 N. Halstead Street,
Pasadena, CA 91107.

of electrometer gain as a function of signal strength,
MS data analysis, and printout of analytical results.
It can automatically quantitate up to 16 different
compounds in complex mixtures.

In this instrument, the assay programs are "cali-
brated" by injection of pure reference standards. The
relative intensities of the mass lines selected for
specific identification of each individual cannabinoid
(7), as well as the quantity scale factor and nominal
retention time for each compound, are thereby entered
into the computer memory. In automatic operation, the
computer instructs the spectrometer to search for the
characteristic fragment ions only during a time window
near the nominal GC retention time for the compound.

Standards

Reference standards were obtained from the Bio-
medical Research Branch, NIDA. In those cases in which
the standards were provided as ethanolic solutions, the
solvent was removed and the residue was redissolved in
dimethylformamide.

Biological Material

Urine specimens were obtained at various time intervals after oral administration of 30 mg doses of
Δ^9-THC to paid human volunteers who were experienced
marijuana users, but who professed to have abstained
for a minimum of one week prior to the experiment.
Urine specimens were also obtained from a study conducted by Professor Reese Jones at the Langley Porter
Clinic, University of California Medical Center in San
Francisco, in which 30 mg doses were administered orally every four hours (210 mg/day) for several days (12).

Procedure

Dried residues of extracts, processed from volumes
of urine containing 25 mg of creatinine, were dissolved
in 50 μl of BSTFA (containing 1% TMCS) in dimethylformamide (1:1) and heated at 70°C for 5 minutes. Five
microliter aliquots were injected into a 180 cm x 0.2
cm ID pyrex column packed with 1.5% OV-17 on 100/120
mesh HP Chromosorb G held isothermally at 275°C with
nitrogen carrier gas flow of 30 ml/minute. Each sample
was automatically screened by PBM for Δ^9-THC and seven
of its metabolites (cf. Figure 9) using assay programs
consisting of 10 carefully selected characteristic ions
for each compound (7).

OLFAX/GC ANALYSIS

TS=207   TI=295
>ETHER EXTRACT (PH 2.5) OF URINE H-13:FRACTION E-II FROM 5 ML URINE.

DELTA-9-THC   +POS   QTY 5.84E- 2   CONF 24   RT   86
CANNABINOL   NEG   QTY 1.97E- 3   CONF 9   RT 105
8B-HO-D9-THC   NEG   QTY 6.32E- 3   CONF 9   RT 117
11-HO-D9-THC   NEG   QTY 6.84E- 3   CONF 11   RT 146
8A,11-DI-HO   NEG   QTY 1.14E- 1   CONF 17   RT 144
8B,11-DI-HO   NEG   QTY 1.73E- 2   CONF 9   RT 173
9-THC-11-OIC   +POS   QTY 1.10E+ 0   CONF 94   RT 225
CBN-11-OIC   +POS   QTY 1.14E+ 0   CONF 37   RT 275

Figure 9.   Computer output for Auto-Assay of silylated weakly polar weak acids (E-II) fraction of enzyme-hydrolyzed human urine. (Report is read as, e.g. Δ^9-THC, positively identified, at a level of 5.84×10^{-2} µg, with a Confidence Index of 24 and a retention time of 86 sec. Chromatographic conditions same as Figure 4.

```
OLFAX/GC ANALYSIS

TS=207  TI=296
>ETHER EXTRACT (PH 2) OF URINE #H-13:  FRACTION E-II FROM 5 ML.


9-THC-11-OIC  +POS   QTY 1.39E+ 0    CONF  52    RT  227


MASS   INTENSITY

  75 C  2.53E- 7
 246 C  4.04E- 9
 265 C  4.86E- 9
 289 C  4.44E- 9
 297    6.20E- 9
 299 C  4.12E- 9
 303    6.00E- 9
 305 C  4.20E- 9
 355    7.88E- 9
 371    2.40E- 8

PLOT Y OR N?Y
#OF DECADES=2

FS=2.53E- 7


        E-2                           E-1                          E0
        +--------2-----------5--------+--------2-----------5--------+
        +
        +
      75C+>>>>>>>>>>>>>>>>>>>>>>>>>>>>>>>>>>>>>>>>>>>>>>>>>>>>>>>>>>>>>>
     246C+>>>>>>
     265C+>>>>>>>>>
     289C+>>>>>>>>
     297 +>>>>>>>>>>>
     299C+>>>>>>
     303 +>>>>>>>>>>>
     305C+>>>>>>
     355 +>>>>>>>>>>>>>>>>
     371 +>>>>>>>>>>>>>>>>>>>>>>>>>>>
        +
        +
        +
```

Figure 10. *Confirmation-mode* Δ⁹-*THC-11-oic acid/TMS analysis of Fraction E-II (same sample as Figure 9) showing 1.39 μg/5 mL of hydrolyzed urine with K = 52 at a retention time of 227 sec. All 10 lines were scanned, but 6 were contaminated.*

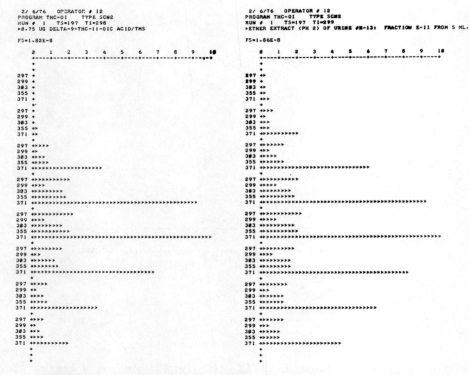

Figure 11. (Right) SICP of Δ⁹-THC-11-oic acid GC peak derived from Fraction
E-II (same sample as Figures 9 and 10). (Left) Same kind of SICP record for
0.75 μg of authentic Δ⁹-THC-11-oic acid (which gave exactly the same signal
strengths).

RESULTS AND DISCUSSION

In a urine specimen obtained from Jones' study
(12), the hexane fraction (H) -- after enzyme hydrolysis -- showed a level of 10 ng of unmetabolized Δ^9-THC
per ml of urine (with a marginally positive Confidence
Index) and 12 ng/ml of cannabinol (CBN) with a high
Confidence Index and hence a clearcut identification.
The weakly polar neutral fraction (E-I) showed a very
marginal positive for CBN at 0.8 ng/ml -- which was
probably due to incomplete extraction by the hexane in
the first step -- and a weakly positive identification
of 8α,11-dihydroxy-Δ^9-THC at 22 ng/ml. The screening
run for the weakly polar, weak acid fraction (E-II) indicated positive identifications for Δ^9-THC (K=24),
Δ^9-THC-11-oic acid (K=94), and CBN-11-oic acid (K=37)
(Figure 9). In the confirmation mode of operation,
which provides a more comprehensive examination of the
data, only the THC-acid was found to be present -- at
1.39 µg/5 ml of urine -- but with six out of the 10
selected ions being contaminated (Figure 10). That the
remaining (uncontaminated ion) intensity ratios were,
in fact, derived from a single substance and that the
ratios do correspond to those of authentic Δ^9-THC-11-
oic acid can be clearly seen in the selected ion current
profiles (SICP) of Figure 11.

When the same procedure was applied to enzyme hydrolyzed urines collected during the interval from 12-
24 hours following a single 30 mg oral dose of Δ^9-THC,
the hexane fraction gave a strongly positive Confidence
Index (K=59) for CBN at 10 ng/ml, but a negative indication for unchanged Δ^9-THC. Very marginal indications
of 8α-hydroxy- and 8α,11-dihydroxy-Δ^9-THC were seen in
fraction E-I. Fraction E-II, the weak acid fraction,
gave an unequivocal identification of Δ^9-THC-oic acid
(K=86) at 5.2 µg per 25 mg creatinine, but CBN-11-oic
acid could not be demonstrated in this sample.

The most significant information in the present
study arises from a radically different approach to
these metabolite investigations. Four years ago, we
reported that an appreciable proportion of the total
radioactivity in Rhesus monkey urine could be extracted
with ether, even without prior hydrolysis (13). This
excretion was highly pH-dependent -- with the curve's
inflection point being near pH 4 (Figure 12) -- indicating that the materials being extracted were probably
carboxylic acids.

Last year as one part of our investigation of the
urines obtained from the Langley Porter Clinic Study,
we extracted a specimen with ether at pH 5.5 before

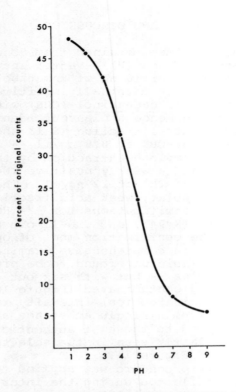

Figure 12. Effect of pH on ether extractability of Δ^9-THC in vivo metabolites from unhydrolyzed Rhesus urine

treatment with enzyme (7). Although this pH is far from the optimum for recovery of Δ^9-THC-11-oic acid using ether, a highly significant Confidence Index (K=62) for the unconjugated Δ^9-THC-11-oic acid at a level of 48 ng/ml was obtained (Figures 13 and 14). When the extraction was made at pH 2.5, nearly double the quantity (90 ng/ml) was measured. Since about 280 ng/ml was extracted at pH 2 after hydrolysis (Figure 10), this level of 90 ng/ml suggests that nearly half of the total Δ^9-THC-11-oic acid that is present in urine can be extracted directly -- without hydrolyzing the specimen (cf. also Figure 2). Accordingly a set of urines was processed, with and without hydrolysis, using our routine solvent fractionation scheme. The E-II fractions from urines collected for the 12 hours pre-drug and from 0-2, 2-6, 6-12, 12-24, 24-48 and 48-72 hours post-drug were assayed by PBM.

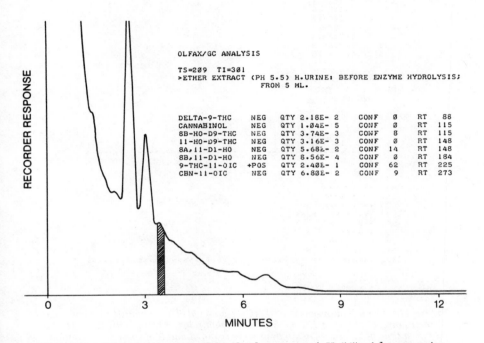

Figure 13. Chromatogram of silylated ether extract (pH 5.5) of human urine prior to enzyme hydrolysis. (Chromatographic conditions same as Figure 4). Shaded area denotes retention time window during which the Olfax searched for the Δ^9-THC-11-oic acid/TMS contracted spectrum. Inset: Auto-Assay analysis for THC panel of 8 compounds in which 240 ng (2.40 × 10⁻¹ µg) of Δ^9-THC-11-oic acid was found with a Confidence Index of 62.

```
OLFAX/GC ANALYSIS

TS=238   TI=295
>ETHER EXTRACT (PH 5.5) H.URINE:   BEFORE ENZYME HYDROLYSIS;
                       FROM 5 ML.


9-THC-11-OIC   +POS   QTY 1.74E- 1    CONF  44     RT  225


MASS  INTENSITY

246 C   5.06E-10
265 C   5.24E-10
289 C   7.32E-10
297     8.40E-10
299 C   4.73E-10
303     8.20E-10
305 C   4.26E-10
355     7.76E-10
371     3.36E- 9

PLOT Y OR N?Y
#OF DECADES=1

FS=3.36E- 9


      0    1    2    3    4    5    6    7    8    9    10
      +----+----+----+----+----+----+----+----+----+----+
      +
      +
  75  +
246C +>>>>>>>>
265C +>>>>>>>>
289C +>>>>>>>>>>>
297  +>>>>>>>>>>>>>>
299C +>>>>>>>
303  +>>>>>>>>>>>>>
305C +>>>>>>
355  +>>>>>>>>>>>>
371  +>>>>>>>>>>>>>>>>>>>>>>>>>>>>>>>>>>>>>>>>>>>>>>>>>>>>
      +
      +
      +
```

Figure 14.   Confirmation-mode Δ^9-THC-11-oic acid/TMS analysis of same sample as Figure 13 showing 174 ng/5 mL of unhydrolyzed urine with $K = 44$ at a retention time of 225 sec. Only 9 lines were scanned and 5 of these were contaminated.

        It was found that the <u>free</u> (unconjugated) Δ^9-THC-
11-oic acid reached a sharp maximum value in the urine
collected during the interval between two and six hours
(Figure 15); simultaneously, the <u>bound</u> (conjugated)
form of the drug increased slowly, reaching its maximum
level in the 6-12 hour collection and falling slowly
thereafter. Again it was found that, from 12 hours on-
ward, the free drug constituted somewhat less than half
of the total Δ^9-THC-11-oic acid. It appears that the
time course of the unconjugated Δ^9-THC-11-oic acid

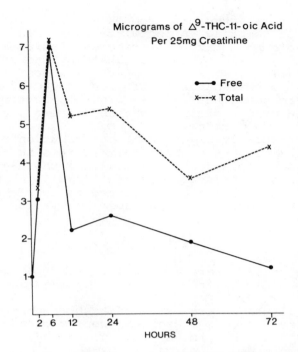

Figure 15. Concentration of Δ⁹-THC-11-oic acid (relative to creatinine) in (●—●, Free), unhydrolyzed urine and (✕---✕, Total), hydrolyzed urine. Note that the free acid reaches a sharp maximum in the urine collected over the interval from 2 to 6 hr after oral administration of pure Δ⁹-THC but that the total acid remains high for several days after dosing.

parallels the blood levels of unmetabolized Δ⁹-THC, as well as ether extractable and total THC metabolites (14), which, in turn, parallel the time course of the psychic effects of Δ⁹-THC (15). All of these parameters peak three hours after oral ingestion of THC.

CONCLUSIONS

Although Δ⁹-THC-11-oic acid is not the most abundant acidic metabolite in urine, its peak levels (hundreds of nanograms per ml) make it a much more accessable form of the drug than free Δ⁹-THC in plasma.

Since our group is no longer engaged in GC/MS studies on THC, only this single experiment has been conducted. Obviously it is risky to extrapolate from

one set of data; however, from these preliminary results, it is tempting to postulate that unconjugated
Δ^9-THC-11-oic acid may be a practical indicator of the
degree of physical impairment caused by the smoking of
marijuana! Thus, if subsequent studies confirm these
findings, the concentration of free Δ^9-THC-11-oic acid
may prove to bear the same relationship to time of ingestion and extent of intoxication as does the urine
concentration of ethanol.

A particularly significant contribution of PBM to
the solution of this problem is that it eliminates the
necessity of sample cleanup and allows the use of crude
ether extracts. Consequently, an Olfax II GC assay for
Δ^9-THC-11-oic acid can be completed in less than 30
minutes from the time a urine specimen is received by
the laboratory.

ACKNOWLEDGMENTS

These studies were made possible by the generous
loan of an Olfax instrument system by the manufacturer,
Vitek Systems, Inc.
Special thanks are extended to Dr. George L. Ellman
of Dr. Reese T. Jones' research group who made available
to us some urine specimens from their study.
This work was supported in part by USPHS Grants
DA00424 and DA00748.

REFERENCES

(1)   Forrest, I. S., Green, D. E., and Wursch, M. S.,
       Abstract #1421, Proc. 5th Intern. Cong. on Phar-
       macol., San Francisco (1972).
(2)   Kanter, S. L., Hollister, L. E., Moore, F. and
       Green, D. E., *Res. Comm. Chem. Path. Pharmacol.*
       9, 205-213 (1974).
(3)   Strauss, P. A. and Hertel, R. H., *J. Chromatogr.*
       134, 39-48 (1977).
(4)   Abramson, F. P., *Anal. Chem. 47*, 45-49 (1975).
(5)   McLafferty, F. W., Hertel, R. H. and Villwock,
       R. D., *Org. Mass Spectrom. 9*, 690-702 (1974).
(6)   Pesyna, G. M., McLafferty, F. W., Venkataraghavan,
       R., and Dayringer, H. E., *Anal. Chem. 47*, 1161-
       1164 (1975).
(7)   Green, D. E., in "Cannabinoid Assays in Humans",
       NIDA Research Monograph No. 7, 1976, pp. 70-87.
(8)   Kanter, S. L., Hollister, L. E., and Moore, F.,
       Res. Comm. Chem. Path. Pharmacol. 10, (2), 215-
       219 (1975).

(9)   Lombrozo, L., Kanter, S. L., and Hollister, L. E.,
      Res. Comm. Chem. Path. Pharmacol., *15* (4), 697–
      703 (1976).
(10) Kanter, S. L., and Hollister, L. E., *Res. Comm.
      Chem. Path. Pharmacol.*, *17* (3), 421–431 (1977).
(11) Hertel, R. H., Green, D. E. and Strauss, P. A.,
      Proc. 26th Pittsburgh Conf. on Anal. Chem. and
      Appl. Spectr. (1975).
(12) Jones, R. T., Benowitz, N., and Bachman, J.,
      Ann. N. Y. Acad. Sci. 282, 221–239 (1973).
(13) Melikian, A. P., Green, D. E., Skinner, J. L.,
      and Forrest, I. S., *Proc. West. Pharmacol. Soc.*
      26,
(14) Lemberger, L., Axelrod, J. and Kopin, J., *Ann.
      N. Y. Acad. Sci. 191*, 142–152 (1971).
(15) Hollister, L. E., Richards, R. K., and Gillespie,
      H. K., *Clin. Pharmacol. Ther. 9*, 783–791 (1968).

RECEIVED December 12, 1978.

HPLC Analysis of Δ^9-Tetrahydrocannabinol and Metabolites in Biological Fluids

SETH R. ABBOTT and JOHN R. BERG—Varian Instrument Division, 2700 Mitchell Drive, Walnut Creek, CA 94598

KAY O. LOEFFLER, SAUL KANTER, and LEO E. HOLLISTER—Veterans Administration Hospital, Palo Alto, CA 94304

JOAN HAWKINS ABRAMS—California School of Professional Psychology, San Francisco, CA 94110

HUGH L. BARAS and REESE T. JONES—Langley-Porter Neuropsychiatric Institute, University of California, San Francisco, CA 94143

High performance liquid chromatography (HPLC) can rapidly separate drugs and metabolites from endogenous compounds in biological fluids. Fractions are readily collected and thus HPLC has been used in cannabinoid work to purify biological fluid extracts prior to analysis by techniques offering either more sensitive or specific detection than has been available for LC. HPLC cleanup of biological fluids has been reported prior to cannabinoid analysis by direct mass spectrometry, (1) GC-mass spectrometry, (Wall, this vol., Clarks, this vol.), GC (2) and radioimmunoassay (Teale, this vol.).

Classical LC detectors (refractive index, fixed wavelength UV absorbance at 254 or 280 nm) have lacked the sensitivity to allow direct analysis of cannabinoids in biological fluids. However, recent development of variable wavelength absorbance detectors extending into the 195-220nm UV region and of fluorescence detectors for HPLC led the authors to initiate

0-8412-0488-8/79/47-098-115$05.50/0

a feasibility study of direct HPLC analysis of cannabinoids in biological fluids. The sensitivity of current
HPLC detectors towards cannabinoids is given in Table 1.
This paper is a progress report on the use of
simultaneous dual wavelength (215nm, 280nm) absorbance
detection for HPLC analysis of cannabinoids in biological fluids. Work in progress on fluorescence detection
of cannabinoids will be the subject of a later report.

TABLE I

HPLC Detection of Cannabinoids

Detector	Sensitivity* in abscence of matrix interference	Selectivity vs.Endogenous Substances
Refractive Index	300 ng	None
254,280 nm	10 ng (THC type) 1 ng (CBN type)	Discriminates against lipids, which do not absorb at 280 nm
215 nm	0.5 ng	≈300-fold dis-crimination against lipids
Fluorescence A. Native Fluorescence	1 ng predicted	Excellent
B. Dansyl derivatives	5 pg (3)	Interference from biologi-cal phenols, 1^O and 2^O amines. Amines interference can be serious

*Sensitivities based on 200µl peak volumes obtained
using 25 cm x 2.1 mm ID analytical HPLC columns.

EXPERIMENTAL

Recovery of Cannabinoids from Human Urine

A volume of urine containing 25mg of creatinine
was hydrolyzed with beta-glucuronidase/aryl sulfatase
and concentrated in a rotary evaporator (5). The
concentrate, diluted to 10ml with distilled water, was
adjusted to pH 8, then extracted with hexane, adjusted
to pH 12 and extracted with ether, and then adjusted to
pH 2.5 and extracted with ether again. The latter
ether extract was extracted three times with 8 ml of 2%
sodium bicarbonate (pH 8.8). The ether phase, containing the more polar acidic metabolites, was adjusted to
pH 2.5 and extracted with ether (5). Each of the organic extracts was evaporated under nitrogen. The
residues were then reconstituted in 50 μl methanol. A
schematic description of the extraction scheme is given
in Figure 1. Studies with urines spiked with radiolabelled standards have shown the cannabinoids to
partition as follows:

```
hexane extract = THC, CBN, CBD, monohydroxy
                 metabolites
E-I extract    = Polyhydroxy metabolites
E-II extract   = Weakly polar acids (e.g. Δ9-THC-
                 11-oic acid)
E-III extract  = More polar acids
```

Recovery of Cannabinoids from Human Breast Milk

A 4 ml sample of milk was hydrolyzed and extracted
according to the urine procedure. The hexane extract
residue was dissolved in 2 ml methanol and centrifuged
at ambient temperature, removing white lipid material.
The methanol was evaporated under nitrogen and the
residue reconstituted in 50 μl hexane.

HPLC

Liquid Chromatography was performed on a Varian
8520 dual syringe pump liquid chromatograph. Two Vari-
chrom™ variable wavelength detectors were used in
series to provide a dual wavelength detection system.
A 25cm x 2.1 mm ID Varian MicroPak MCH-10 column, prepared by chemically bonding a monomolecular layer of

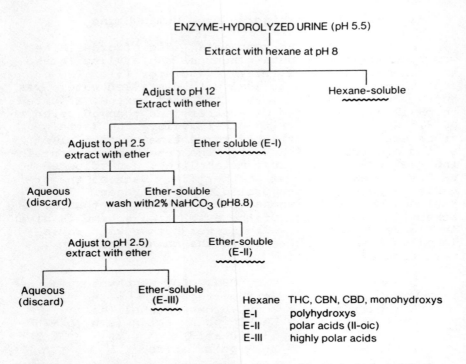

Figure 1. Schematic of extraction scheme for cannabinoids in biological fluids

octadecyl onto 10 micron silica gel, was used for the separation of the urine extracts. A similar size Varian MicroPak CN-10 column, prepared by chemically bonding a monomolecular layer of cyanopropyl groups onto 10 micron silica gel was used for separation of the milk extract.

ANALYSIS OF URINE

Results

    Urine samples collected from two human subjects, prior to (minus 24 to 0 hours) and after (plus 2 to 6 hours) oral administration of 30 mg Δ^9-THC, were hydrolyzed and extracted as described in the experimental section. Pre- and post-drug extracts corresponding to equivalent urinary creatinine levels were separated by reverse phase HPLC. The pre-drug extract was used as a "blank", characteristic of the endogenous composition of the subject's urine.

A MicroPak[TM] MCH-10 reverse phase column was chosen for separation of the hexane and ether extracts. The monomolecular C_{18} bonded phase provides efficient separation of both polar and non-polar substances and rapid equilibration to initial activity after gradient elution programs. The reverse phase column provides symmetrical, narrow peaks for the cannabinoic acids, which tend to tail on polar, normal phase columns (e.g. silica).

Use of a water-acetonitrile mobile phase system allowed detection below 220nm; the Δ^9-THC extinction coefficient is ca. 30 fold greater at 215nm than 280nm (and the matrix interference was less at 215nm). Thus, Δ^9-THC detectivity of the HPLC system with 215nm detection was superior to that at 280nm by an order of magnitude.

Endogenous substances in the extracts are more polar than the cannabinoids and elute before them on the reverse phase column. On polar, normal phase columns, strong adsorption of endogenous species requires periodic column clean-up. This problem was not encountered with the reverse phase gradient system.

Separations were monitored with variable wavelength detectors set at 215nm and 280nm respectively. The A_{215}/A_{280} absorbance ratio acts as a valuable check on extract peaks having retention times coincident with cannabinoid standards. The A_{215}/A_{280} ratios of several cannabinoid standards[1] are listed in Table 2. The cannabinoids segregate into two classes based on the A_{215}/A_{280} ratio. The THC class has a high absorbance ratio (24-37), reflecting the relatively weak 280nm absorbance ($\varepsilon \simeq 1500$) of the phenolic ring. The CBN class has a low absorbance ratio ($\simeq 2$) reflecting the strong 280nm absorbance ($\varepsilon \simeq 18,000$) of a hydroxybiphenyl ring system.

1. Hexane Extract, Subject 1

The 215nm chromatograms of the pre- and post-drug hexane extracts equivalent to 5 mg creatinine (29 ml urine) are shown in Figure 2. In the 5%B/min.water → acetonitrile gradient, available standards ranging from the relatively polar Δ^9-THC-11-oic acid to the nonpolar Δ^9-THC eluted between ≈10-14 minutes (50→70% acetonitrile). More polar cannabinoids such as hydroxy acids

These ratios are sensitive to detector calibration and should always be determined on a given dual detector system by monitoring the chromatography of standards.

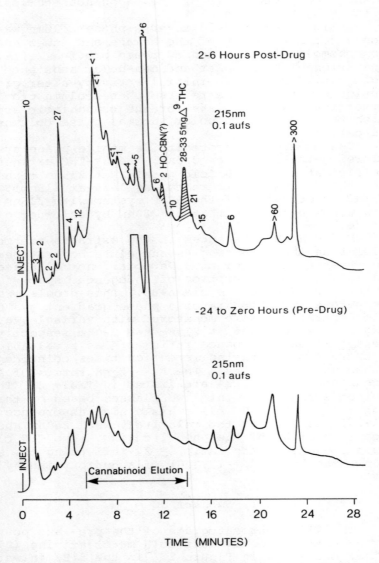

Figure 2. The 215-nm chromatograms of hexane extracts of urine of subject 1, pre- and post-dose. A MicroPak MCH-10 column with 1 mL/min linear gradient program from water → acetonitrile at +5% B/min.

TABLE 2

A_{215}/A_{280} *Absorbance Ratios of Cannabinoids*

Cannabinoid	Absorbance Ratio	
Δ^9-THC	28.6	
Δ^9-THC	23.8	
CBD	35.9	
8β-OH-Δ^9-THC	36.5	THC Class
11-OH-Δ^9-THC	37.0	
8, 11-di-OH -Δ^9-THC	35.2	
Δ^9-11-oic Acid	28.1	
CBN	2.2	CBN Class
CBN-11-oic Acid	1.7	

should elute earlier. The 5-14 minute (25→70% acetonitrile) region was thus estimated to be the cannabinoid
elution region. This region was screened for peaks
with retention times and absorbance ratios coincident
with available standards and for peaks not matching
retention times of standards but having THC or CBN-
type ratios.

A peak was observed coincident with the Δ^9-THC retention time in the post-drug extract chromatogram.
The THC region was blank in the pre-drug extract
chromatogram.

The 215 and 280nm chromatograms of the post-drug
extract are shown in Figure 3. The suspected Δ^9-THC
peak had an A_{215}/A_{280} ratio of 28-33. The uncertainty
in measurement was due to the weakness of the 280nm
peak. The Δ^9-THC standard had a ratio of 28.6. The
peak was thus assigned to Δ9-THC. The peak absorbance
and 215nm extinction coefficient of Δ^9-THC indicate
5lng injected onto the column, which extrapolates to
1.26 µg and 1.7 ppb Δ^9-THC in the +2 to 6 hour urine
(125mg creatinine, 719ml urine).

A peak was observed in the cannabinoid region of
the post-drug extract which had a CBN-type ratio of 2.
The region was clear in the pre-drug extract. The peak
retention time did not match any of the available
standards. Its elution time suggests that it is less
polar than 8β-OHΔ^9-THC and slightly more polar than
CBD.[1]

---

[1]The retention order of the natural, neutral cannabinoids on the reversed phase column is CBD-CBN-THC with
the THC the most retained.

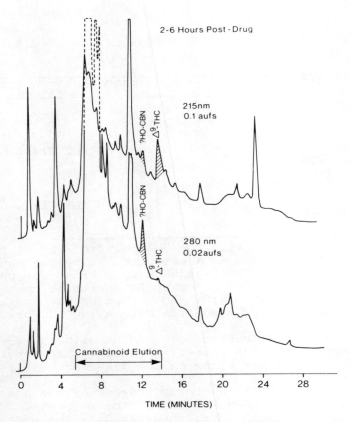

Figure 3. The 215- and 280-nm chromatograms of post drug hexane extract of urine of subject 1. MicroPak MCH-10 column with 1 mL/min linear gradient program from water → acetonitrile at +5% B/min.

2.   *Hexane Extract, Subject 2*

A hexane extract of the urine of a second subject was analyzed to see if the CBN-class peak repeated. The pre- and post-drug hexane equivalents to 5mg creatinine of another subject were separated using a slower gradient (3%B/min) than that used for Subject 1.   The 215nm cannabinoid elution region is shown in Figure 4B, side by side with that of the Subject 1 urine in Figure 4A.   The 3%B/min gradient gave somewhat better resolution of endogenous material from the cannabinoid region and is the preferred program for the hexane extract.

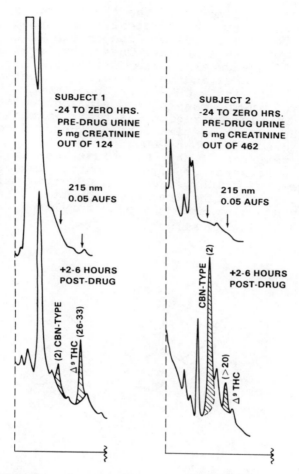

*Figure 4.   The 215-nm chromatograms of hexane extracts of urines of subjects 1
and 2, pre- and post-dose. MicroPak MCH-10 column with 1 mL/min linear
gradient program from water → acetonitrile at 3% B/min.*

Again, a peak was observed in the Subject 2 post-drug urine coincident with the Δ^9-THC retention time. Its absorbance ratio was greater than 20. A closer estimate was precluded by the weakness of the 280nm absorbance. Its elution region was blank in the pre-drug urine. The peak was thus assigned to Δ^9-THC and corresponds to 15ng injected onto the column, which extrapolates to 1.39 µg and 4 ppb Δ^9-THC in the +2-6 hour urine (462mg creatinine, 347 ml urine).

   The HPLC estimates of the Δ^9-THC levels, based on
the 215nm extinction coefficient, correspond to excretion of 0.004 and 0.005% of dose in the +2 to 6 hour
urines of subjects 1 and 2. These levels agree with
previous TLC analyses of other urines of these patients.
   As was the case in the post-drug extract of subject 1, a peak with a CBN-class absorbance ratio of 2
was observed in the cannabinoid elution region of subject 2.   Its elution region was blank in the pre-drug
urine. The retention time again suggests a compound
slightly more polar than CBD.
   The appearance of this CBN-class peak in the post-
drug urines of both subjects and concomitant absence
in the pre-drug urines suggests a CBN-type metabolite
of Δ^9-THC. The metabolite retention time suggests a
relatively nonpolar side-chain hydroxylated CBN (I) or
a cannabinodiol type structure (II).

(I)

(II).

The cannabinodiol hypothesis is interesting in that previous gas chromatography-mass fragmentography (GC-MF) analyses of similar urines from our lab (9) consistently detected a compound having a GLC retention time ca. 8% greater than that of CBN, but with the characteristic mass fragments of CBN. Cannabinodiol was observed by van Ginneken et al (10)→(7) to have a cannabinol-like mass fragmentation pattern. It should be noted that van Ginneken did not isolate cannibinodiol for spectral analysis and thus one is not certain of its A_{215}/A_{280} ratio. It is possible that steric hindrance of the isopropenyl and nearby phenolic hydroxyl could reduce co-planarity of the biphenyl rings, altering the absorbance ratio from that expected for a CBN compound.

If the unidentified peak had a characteristic CBN extinction coefficient at 215nm ($\varepsilon \approx 37,500$), one calculates its level to be 0.7ppb in the urine of subject 1 and 21ppb in the urine of subject 2.

3. EII Extract, Subject 1

The 215nm chromatograms of the pre- and post-drug EII ether extracts (see Figure 1) equivalent to 2.5mg creatinine are shown in Figure 5. The EII extract is of interest because of recent work by Greene (this volume) in which the ratio of bound to unbound urinary Δ^9-THC-11-oic acid, the major known THC metabolite in humans, was proposed to be a function of time after dose. As described in the experimental section, this acid partitions into the EII fraction.

A peak was observed coincident with the retention time of Δ^9-THC-11-oic acid, having an absorbance ratio of 26-32 in the post-drug extract. Its elution area was blank in the pre-drug chromatogram.

The peak was thus assigned to Δ^9-THC-11-oic acid and represents 98ng injected, which extrapolates to 4.85 μg and 6.7ppb in the +2-6 hour urine. Silica gel TLC analysis of this urine extract indicated a Δ^9-11-oic acid level of ca. 6 μg. The TLC level was obtained by visual estimation of the Fast Blue Salt (B) (FBSB) spot intensity. The agreement of HPLC and TLC was thus excellent.

The relatively large excretion of Δ^9-THC-11-oic acid in humans and the low 215nm matrix level of the EII ether extract makes rapid, direct HPLC-215nm absorbance analysis relatively simple. The fast 5%B/min gradient program (20 minute analysis) is acceptable for this application.

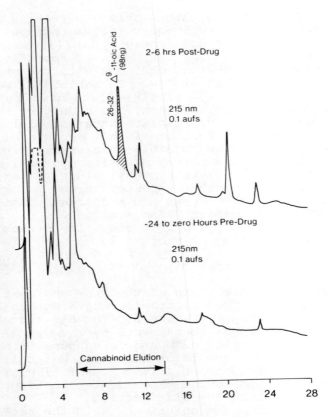

Figure 5.   The 215-nm chromatograms of E-II ether extracts of urine of subject 1,
pre- and post-dose. MicroPak MCH-10 column with 1 mL/min linear gradient
program from water → acetonitrile at 5% B/min.

E-I Ether Extract, Subject 1

The 215nm chromatograms of the pre- and post-drug
E-I ether extracts equivalent to 2.5 mg creatinine are
shown in Figure 6. The EI extract should contain neutral, polyhydroxy metabolites. Peaks with retention
times coincident with the available 8, 11-dihydroxy-
Δ^9-THC standards were not observed in the post-drug
extract. However, a series of five peaks with absorbance ratios of 1.6 - 3.7 was detected. These peaks
were not present in the pre-drug urine. These A_{215}/A_{280}
ratios suggest CBN-type compounds.

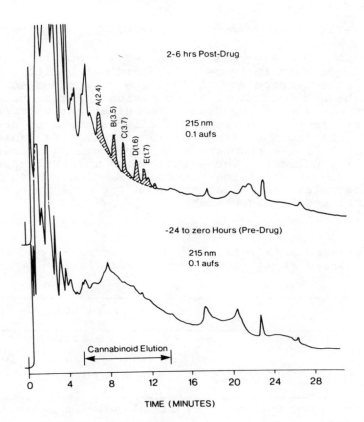

Figure 6. 215-nm chromatograms of E-I ether extracts of urine of subject 1, pre-and post-dose. MicroPak MCH-10 column with 1 mL/min linear gradient program from water → acetonitrile at 5% B/min.

Previous silica gel TLC studies of E-I extracts of subject urines showed a series of five unidentified spots in the mono-polyhydroxy R_f region. The spots stained magenta with FBSB spray regent. At this time, we can merely speculate that the series of HPLC peaks may be CBN-type metabolic products of Δ^9-THC. We did not have hydroxy-CBN standards (8, 11 or side-chain) to compare against the suspect HPLC or TLC species. We do not understand why the TLC spots stain magenta with FBSB, usually characteristic of THC class compounds, while the HPLC peaks had characteristic CBN-type absorbance ratios.

5. E-III Ether Extract, Subject 1

The chromatograms of the E-III fraction which should contain the more polar acid metabolites, had too much interference from endogenous substances to allow cannabinoid detection. A comparison of the endogenous matrix levels of the hexane and ether extracts, expressed in terms of relative 215nm absorbance area in the cannabinoid elution region, is given in Table 3. The bulk of the endogenous urinary material occurs in the EIII extract. These endogenous matrix levels highlight the value of the Kanter extraction scheme in providing relatively clean extracts for analysis of the neutral and 11-oic cannabinoids.

TABLE 3

Endogenous Matrix Level of Urine Extracts of Subject 1 Based on A_{215}, in Cannabinoid Elution Region

	A_{215} Values
Hexane extract	1.0 relative unit*
E-I	3.3
E-II	2.2
E-III	76.9

*1.0 relative unit = 34 μg cannabinoid in extract

B. Discussion

Direct HPLC analysis of urine extracts appears feasible for Δ^9-THC. 215nm is the optimum wavelength for detection of THC-class compounds. Dual wavelength at 215 and 280nm serves as a valuable check on cannabinoid retention assignment and as a screen for unknown THC or CBN-class metabolites. The latter feature was demonstrated in the observance of CBN-class peaks in both hexane and E-I extracts. This observation suggests a CBN-metabolic route of Δ^9-THC. Evidence of a CBN-metabolic route for Δ^9-THC has been reported by McCallum (8) and Green (6) for humans and by Ben Zvi et al (9) for rhesus monkeys.

An improvement in the HPLC method should be realized by collection of the cannabinoid elution region of the reverse phase separation followed by normal phase chromatography of the fraction. This should allow use of the excellent selectivity of the normal phase

column towards polar metabolites while avoiding the
problem of excessive adsorption of endogenous substances encountered when injecting unpurified extracts
onto a normal phase column.

ANALYSIS OF BREAST MILK

    Results

    A four milliliter sample of breast milk was donated
by a chronic cannabis user whose 6 month old male infant was participating in a study evaluating the effect
of maternal cannabis use on infant development (10).
The mother had an estimated THC intake of 25-50 mg
during a 3-4 hour period prior to milk collection. The
milk was expressed approximately 15 minutes after ces-
sation of smoking.
    The milk sample was hydrolzyed and extracted as
described in the experimental section. The hexane extract was then analyzed for the presence of neutral,
nonpolar cannabinoids, (Δ^8 and Δ^9-THC, CBN, CBN). Breast
milk contains 2-6% fats, the exact content varying with
maternal diet. Hexane extracts a large amount of fat
from the milk, making analysis of trace cannabinoids in
this matrix difficult. Triglycerides, the major lipid
components of milk, are difficult to elute from reverse
phase columns and thus a normal phase separation was
used for the milk extract.
    To reduce interference from endogenous fats, the
extract was partially purified by chromatographing five
successive 20µl extract injections (equivalent to 0.5
ml milk each) on a MicroPak CN-10 column. A gradient
elution program from hexane to 5% methanol in dichloromethane was used for the purification step. The
elution region corresponding to the neutral nonpolar
cannabinoids was collected from each run. The fractions were then combined and analyzed on another
MicroPak CN-10 column.
    Separate columns were used for extract purification
and analysis because successive injections of the highly concentrated, fatty extract gradually reduces column
efficiency. Thus, the analytical column should be subjected to as clean a sample as possible.
    The analytical separation was obtained at low flow
velocity (0.2 cm/sec) and in the isocratic mode to op-
timize resolution. Absorbance detectors set at 245 and
280nm respectively, were used in series for effluent
monitoring. 215nm detection, though optimum for the
cannabinoids, was precluded due to co-elution of en-

dogenous fats still present at relatively high levels in the partially purified extract.

An isocratic CN column separation of cannabinoid standards is shown in Figure 7. Note the excellent separation of the Δ^8 and Δ^9-THC isomers. The CN column has been found to be useful in separation of double bond isomers, presumably due to interactions with the nitrile group of the cyano bonded phase. The chromatogram of the partially purified hexane extract of 1.5 ml milk is shown in Figure 8. Peaks were not observed in the Δ^8-THC, CBN or CBN regions. However, an intense, sharp peak was observed at the retention time of Δ^9-THC, having the appropriate A_{245}/A_{280} absorbance ratio of 1.5.

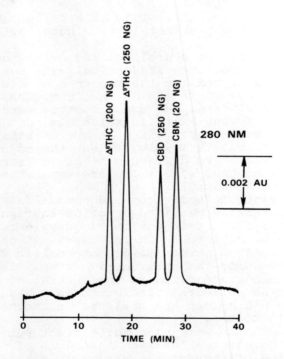

Figure 7. Separation of natural, neutral cannabinoids on MicroPak CN-10 column with 0.25 mL/min 3% B isocratic: solvent A = hexane; solvent B = 5% methanol in dichloromethane.

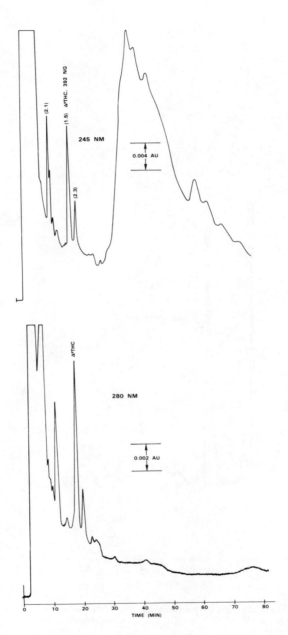

Figure 8. Chromatogram of partially purified hexane extract of 1.5 mL breast milk. MicroPak CN-10 column with 0.25 mL/min 3% B isocratic: solvent A = hexane; solvent B = 5% methanol in dichloromethane.

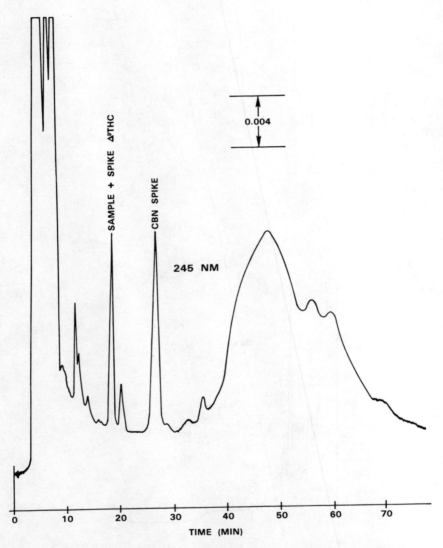

Figure 9. Chromatogram of partially purified hexane extract of 0.7 mL breast milk, co-injected with Δ⁹-THC and CBN standard (same conditions as Figure 7)

An extract of 0.7 ml breast milk was then co-
injected with Δ^9-THC (200 ng) and CBN (100 ng) standard.
A single, sharp peak was observed at the Δ^9-THC retention time (Figure 9). Approximately half the peak absorbance is due to the spike and half to the milk
sample. The separation of the THC and CBN peaks had
remained constant, indicating that column activity had
not changed.
    Positive identification of the suspected THC peak
requires future isolation of the species from larger
milk volumes, followed by off-line spectral analysis
(NMR, IR, MS). At this time, the retention match, absorbance ratio match and spike test in a high resolution HPLC separation support a tentative identification
of Δ^9-THC in the milk.
    If the suspected peak of Figure 8 is Δ^9-THC, its
absorbance value indicates a milk level of 0.26 µg/ml.
This extrapolates to an oral intake of 26 µg THC during
an average 100 ml feeding, corresponding to 0.05-0.10%
of the mother's estimated THC intake.

    Discussion

    Cannabinoids have been detected in the milk of
ewes and squirrel monkeys following administration of
Δ^9-THC. Jakubovic et al (11) recovered 0.03-0.05% of
applied radioactivity in the milk of ewes given ^{14}C-Δ^9-
THC. Milks collected periodically between 4 - 96 hours
after drug administration all contained radioactivity.
The highest level occurred in the 4 hour sample. Most
of the milk radioactivity corresponded to a species in
the petroleum ether extract having the same R_f and FBSB
color as Δ^9-THC on thin-layer chromatography (TLC).
Leighty et al (12) speculated that this species, occurring in the milk at long periods after dose, may
have been a fatty acid conjugate of 11-hydroxy-Δ^9-THC.
    Jakubovic et al (11) detected radioactivity in
suckled rats after administration of ^{14}C-Δ^9-THC to the
mothers. TLC showed Δ^9-THC to be present in the infant
brain. Electron microscopy of the infant brains showed
a reduction in the number of ribosomes attached to the
nuclear membrane of the brain cells. Hattoric et al
(13) observed a similar effect after administration of
Δ^9-THC directly to infant rats. These results suggested significant transfer of Δ^9-THC into the milk.
    Chao et al (14) recovered 0.2% of applied radio-
activity in the milk of lactating squirrel monkeys
given ^{14}C-Δ^9-THC. Milks were collected periodically
between 1-24 hours after drug administration. Peak

levels of radioactivity occurred between 2-4 hours.
0.01% of the radioactivity was identified as Δ^9-THC by
TLC. Most of the radioactivity corresponded to metabolites having R_f values in the mono- and dihydroxy region. However, R_f matches with standards were not
obtained. Differences were not found between milk
volume of control and THC-monkeys or between weight
gain of infants nursed by control and THC-monkeys.

Although animal studies indicate transfer of Δ^9-
THC into the milk, comparable research has not been
done on humans. It is difficult to extrapolate from
animal studies to humans. The only primates studied,
squirrel monkeys, are known to metabolize Δ^9-THC dif-
ferently than humans. (15) In addition, lactating
human mothers in the general population ingest both
Δ^9-THC and other cannabinoids (e.g., CBN, CBD) by smoking cannabis. Information is not currently available
regarding either transfer of cannabinoids into the milk
of lactating humans or the effects of maternal cannabis
use on infant development.

Several factors suggest the possibility of THC
transfer into the milk of humans. Hollister et al (16)
found unmetabolized Δ^9-THC in human urines between 0-6
hours after a 30 mg dose. Total urinary THC recovered
was 0.005 to 0.01% of dose. We report similar HPLC
results in this paper. Plasma Δ^9-THC levels of 100-
300 ng/ml have been measured in humans after smoking
three 20 mg Δ^9-THC cigarettes. (17) Transfer of drugs
from plasma into the milk is facilitated by high lipid
solubility of the drug, and Δ^9-THC is a strong lipo-
phile.

The HPLC result reported here suggests a transfer
of Δ^9-THC into the breast milk of a <u>chronic</u> cannabis
user. The calculated level of 0.26 µg/ml extrapolates
to 26 µg per average 100 ml feeding which corresponds
to 0.05-0.10% of the mother's estimated THC intake. It
should be noted that this analysis was on a <u>single</u> sample and has not yet been confirmed by off-line spectral
characterization. The identification of Δ^9-THC in the
milk must therefore be regarded as tentative. Future
work requires multiple sample analyses from both average and chronic users. The milk should be analyzed for
both Δ^9-THC and metabolites.

The pharmacologically active hydroxy metabolites,
present either as free or as fatty acid conjugates,
will be of prime interest. Sufficient milk volume must
be collected to allow HPLC isolation of suspected cannabinoids and off-line mass spectral characterization.
A successful interfacing of an HPLC to a mass spectrometer would greatly simplify this work.

The significance of transfer of cannabinoids into human breast milk depends on whether it occurs at levels sufficient to elicit physiological or behavioral effects in a nursing infant. Comprehensive development studies of the infants of mothers using cannabis during pregnancy and/or lactation are required. Such studies are now in progress. (14).

ACKNOWLEDGEMENT

This work was supported in part by grants DA 00424 and 5R01 DA 00748 and the research service of the Veterans Administration, by the National Institute of Alcohol, Drug Abuse and Mental Health Administration, National Research Service Award Number 1 F32 DA 05051 of the National Institute on Drug Abuse and by Contract No. HSM-42-73-181 from the National Institute on Drug Abuse, NIDA Research Scientist Award No. 1 KO 5 DA 00053-01. The cannabinoid standards were provided by the National Institute on Drug Abuse of the Department of Health, Education and Welfare. We wish to acknowledge Keith Muir of the University of California, San Francisco, for his helpful discussion of the transfer of drugs into breast milk.

REFERENCES

(1)   Valentine, J. L., Bryant, P. J., Gutshall, P. L., Gan, O. M., Thompson, E. D., and Niu, H., "Cannabinoid Assays in Humans", NIDA Research Monograph No. 7, Rockville, Maryland, 1976, p. 96.

(2)   Garrett, E. R., and Hunt, C. A., *J. Pharm. Sci.* *66*, 20 (1977).

(3)   Abbott, S. R., Abu-Shumays, A., Loeffler, K. O., and Forrest, I. S., *Res. Comm. Chem. Path. Pharmacol. 10, 9* (1975).

(4)   Kanter, S. L., Hollister, L. E., Moore, F., and Green, D. E., *Res. Comm. Chem. Path. Pharmacol. 7, 79* (1974).

(5)   Kanter, S. L., Hollister, L. E., Moore, F., and Green, D. E., *Res. Comm. Chem. Path. Pharmacol. 9, 205* (1974).

(6)   Green, D. E., "Cannabinoid Assays in Humans", NIDA Research Monograph No. 7, Rockville, Maryland, 1976, p. 70.

(7)   Van Ginneken, C. A. M., Vree, T. B., Breimier, D. D., Thyssen, H. W. H., and Van Rossum, J. M., *Proc. Int. Symp. Gas Chromatogr. Mass Spectrom. 111,* (1972).

(8)   McCallum, N. K., *J. Chrom. Sci. 11*, 509   (1973).

(9)   Ben-Zvi, Z., Beyer, J. R., and Bernstein, S., *Res. Comm. Chem. Path. Pharmacol. 9*, (1) 201 (1974).

(10)   Abrams, J. H., Doctoral Dissertation, in Progress, The Effects of Cannabis on Infant Development, California School of Professional Psychology.

(11)   Jakubovic, A., Tait, R. M., and McGeer, P. L., *Tox. Appl. Pharm. 28*, 38   (1974).

(12)   Leighty, E. G., Fentiman, A. F., Jr., and Foltz, R. L., *Res. Comm. Chem. Path. Pharmacology 14*, 13   (1976).

(13)   Jakubovic, A., Hattori, T., and McGar, P. L., *Eur. J. Pharmacol. 22*, 221   (1973).

(14)   Chao, F. C., Green, D. E., Forrest, I. S., Kaplan, J. N., Winship-Ball, A., and Braude, M., *Res. Comm. Chem. Path. Pharm. 15*, 303   (1976).

(15)   Melikian, A. P., Green, D. E., Skinner, J. L., Forrest, I. S., *Proc. West. Pharmacol. Soc. 16*, 234   (1973).

(16)   Hollister, L. E., Kanter, S. L., Board, R. D., and Green, D. E., *Res. Comm. Chem. Path. Pharm. 8*, 579   (1974).

(17)   Gross, S. J., and Soares, J. R., "Cannabinoids Assays in Humans", NIDA Research Monograph No. 7, Rockville, Maryland, 1976, p. 10.

RECEIVED December 12, 1978.

Radioimmunoassay of Cannabinoid Compounds

C. E. COOK

Chemistry and Life Sciences Division, Research Triangle Institute, Research Triangle Park, NC 27709

Radioimmunoassay (or RIA) was first introduced as an analytical technique in 1959. Since then it has played an increasingly important role in the quantitative analysis of hormones and drugs. Much of the recent rapid progress in endocrinology may in fact be attributed to the availability of this sensitive and accurate method for quantitation of steroidal and protein/peptide hormones.

Since radioimmunoassay has permitted the quantitation of substances present in concentrations as low as a few pg/ml of a biological fluid, and since the inherent selectivity of antibodies often make sample preparation requirements minimal and assay methodology simple, RIA has naturally been considered as a means for measuring blood levels of cannabinoid compounds. A number of investigators have been interested in the development of RIA procedures for the cannabinoids.

Before beginning a discussion of the RIA of cannabinoid compounds, let us briefly review some general principles of radioimmunoassay. Figure 1 illustrates the basic premise of RIA. A radiolabeled substance, the antigen or radioligand, binds to an antibody. Addition of unlabeled antigen results in a competition with the radioligand for binding sites, thus reducing the fraction of radioactivity which is bound to the antibody. By measuring either the free or bound radioactivity and establishing a standard curve, one can then determine the amount of antigen present in an unknown sample.

The first step in the development of an RIA pro-

0-8412-0488-8/79/47-098-137$05.00/0

cedure therefore involves getting antibodies which
will bind the compound in question. Furthermore, antibodies which selectively bind the drug to be analyzed are often most desirable since they permit analysis with less for extensive sample preparation.

A second step in RIA development is choice of
the appropriate radioligand. Much of this paper will
be devoted to these two aspects of RIA.

LABELED + SPECIFIC ⇌ LABELED   ANTIGEN-
ANTIGEN   ANTIBODY   ANTIBODY   COMPLEX

+

UNLABELED
ANTIGEN

⇅

UNLABELED ANTIGEN-
ANTIBODY COMPLEX

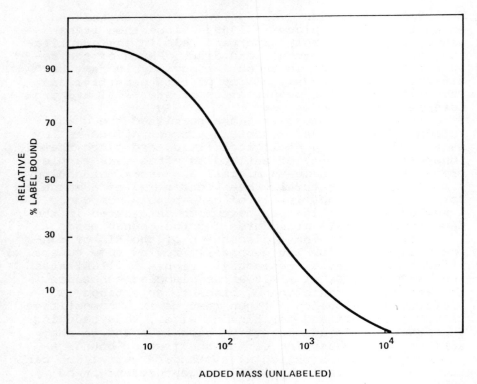

ADDED MASS (UNLABELED)

Raven Press

Figure 1. Basic premise of RIA (13)

IMMUNOGEN SYNTHESIS - GENERAL PRINCIPLES

First let us look at antibody formation as illustrated in Figure 2. Small molecules in general do not
elicit an immune response when injected into animals.
This situation, which is fortunate from the standpoint
of therapeutic use of drugs, presents a substantial
problem for the analyst who wants to assay them. However, in the early 1900's Landsteiner (1) showed that
if small molecules which in themselves were not immunogenic were covalently bonded to a large molecule such
as a protein, the resulting substance (the conjugate)
was immunogenic. Antibodies formed by injection of
animals with this hapten-protein conjugate were found
to selectively bind the original small molecule with
very high affinity.

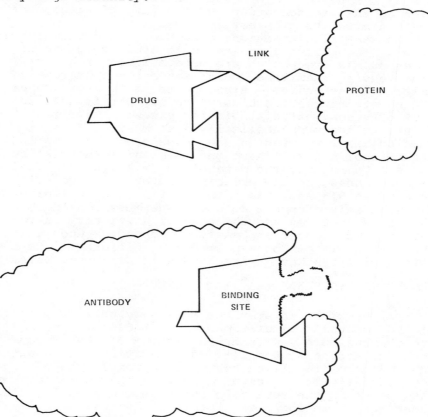

*Figure 2.   Schematic of (top), hapten-protein conjugate and (bottom), antibody
binding site*

The fit between antibody and antigen is often quite good, particularly in areas which are removed from the site of attachment to the protein. However, introduction of the covalent link inevitably results in a change in the structural characteristics of the molecule, and the resulting antibody often reflects this change as is illustrated by the fuzzy area in the figure. Indeed the binding site can emcompass not only the original small molecule but the linkage itself and even portions of the attached protein. In certain instances it has been shown that the drug plus link is bound with much greater affinity than the drug alone, at least by a certain population of antibodies present in the antiserum. Thus, no linking group can be considered inert, and there is no ideal location for linkage of a drug to the protein. However, careful selection of the linkage group and the site of attachment may minimize the problems involved.

In general, in designing a mode of linkage of the drug to the protein, one tries to avoid covering up sites on the drug which are metabolically reactive—thus leaving them free to influence the formation of selective antibodies. Also one tries to avoid covering up structural features which may permit development of strong affinity binding sites. The first point, to leave metabolically active sites free, is particularly important since in general the drug and its metabolites will have many similar structural features. Therefore, the metabolites will, under usual circumstances, be the principal interfering constituents in an RIA analysis. In addition, in designing the synthesis of the immunogen, one must consider the chemistry involved and the ease or difficulty in relation to the expected benefit. Depending upon their needs then, it can be expected that different investigators will synthesize immunogens in different ways.

IMMUNOGEN SYNTHESIS -Δ^8-and Δ^9-THC

As described in previous papers by Wall (2), most of the metabolic alterations of Δ^9-THC occur in the cyclohexane moiety with hydroxylation of the Δ^9-compound occurring at the 11- and 8-positions along with conversion of the 11-carbon to a carboxyl group. More recently it has been found that hydroxylation can also occur in the amyl side chain of the phenolic ring. These latter metabolites exhibit biological activity, but results from Dr. Wall's group in our laboratory indicate that in humans, at least, they are quantitatively minor metabolites.

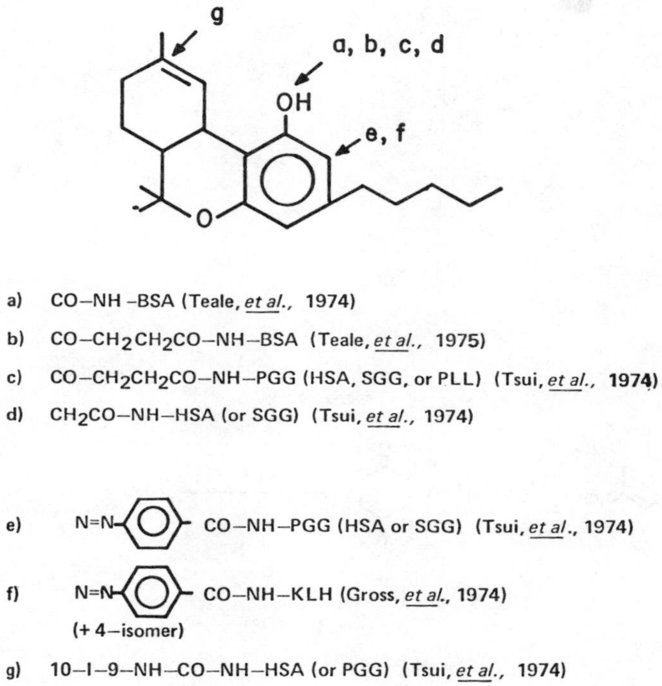

a)   CO—NH—BSA (Teale, *et al.*, 1974)

b)   CO—CH$_2$CH$_2$CO—NH—BSA (Teale, *et al.*, 1975)

c)   CO—CH$_2$CH$_2$CO—NH—PGG (HSA, SGG, or PLL) (Tsui, *et al.*, 1974)

d)   CH$_2$CO—NH—HSA (or SGG) (Tsui, *et al.*, 1974)

e)   N=N—⬡— CO—NH—PGG (HSA or SGG) (Tsui, *et al.*, 1974)

f)   N=N—⬡— CO—NH—KLH (Gross, *et al.*, 1974)

(+ 4—isomer)

g)   10—I—9—NH—CO—NH—HSA (or PGG) (Tsui, *et al.*, 1974)

Figure 3.   Some positions through which Δ^9-THC *has been linked to protein (3)*

A number of previously reported immunogens are
summarized in Figure 3.   Teale, Marks and their co-
workers have prepared immunogens by forming a hemiester
linkage with the phenolic hydroxyl group and coupling
this compound to bovine serum albumin (4, 5).   Tsui
and co-workers (6) also formed a hemisuccinate and a
carboxymethyl ether from the phenolic hydroxyl.   These
products were coupled to a variety of proteins.   The
phenolic group apparently undergoes no metabolic alter-
nations but would be expected to bind well to an antibody, and spatially the attachment to protein is relatively close to the metabolically important cyclohexene
ring.   To avoid this problem Tsui et al. also prepared
a 2-azophenylcarboxy derivative.   This substitution
had been previously employed by Soares, Gross and co-
workers (7).   Finally, Tsui et al. (6) also prepared
a 10-iodo-9-ureido linked THC.
    Our attention was drawn to the amyl side chain of
the aromatic ring as a potential position for attachment to the protein.   Such a linkage would fulfill the

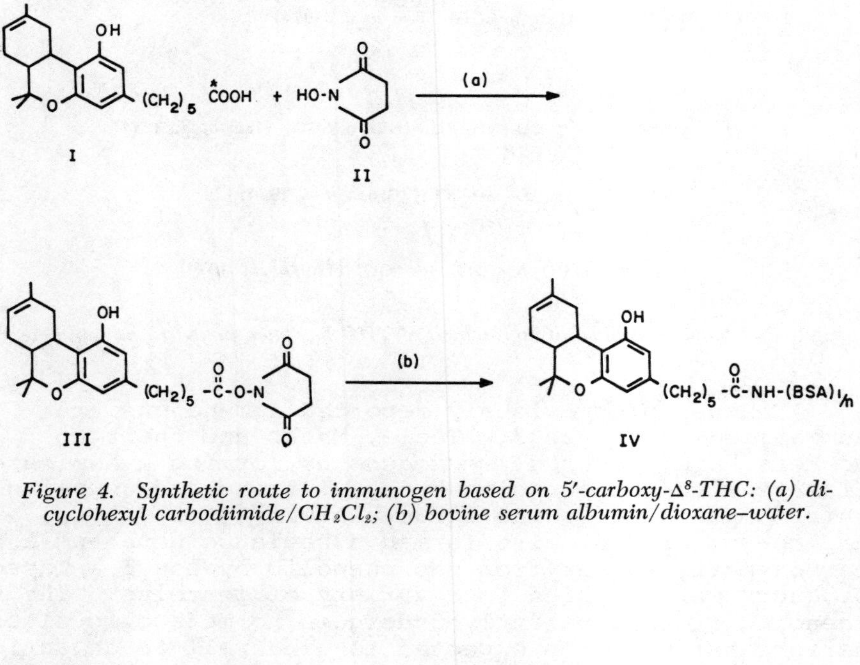

Figure 4. Synthetic route to immunogen based on 5'-carboxy-Δ^8-THC: (a) dicyclohexyl carbodiimide/CH_2Cl_2; (b) bovine serum albumin/dioxane–water.

requirement of distance from the metabolically reactive cyclohexane ring, although not, of course, from sites of hydroxylation on the amyl side chain. For synthetic reasons our initial attempts dealt with the Δ^8-THC analog as a substrate.

Synthesis of the Δ^8-THC antigen is shown in Figure 4. 5'-Carboxy-Δ^8-THC labeled with tracer amounts of carbon-14 in the carboxyl group (8) was converted to a reactive ester by treatment with N-hydroxy-succinimide and dicyclohexylcarbodiimide. This active ester was readily coupled with bovine serum albumin in a mixture of dioxane and water to yield the desired antigen. Radioactivity measurements indicated the incorporation of about 33 residues of Δ^8-THC/molecule of bovine serum albumin. We have found this mode of coupling to be a very useful one, as it is relatively easy to consistently control the number of molecules of drug moiety incorporated into the protein.

ANTISERUM CHARACTERIZATION

Rabbits were immunized with the conjugate (dissolved in sterile sodium chloride solution and homogenized with an equal volume of Freund's complete adjuvant). Immunization with 200 µg of antigen was carried out by the intradermal technique of Vaitukaitis et al. (9), followed after two weeks by another intradermal immunization and then at four week intervals by subcutaneous booster injections. The animals were bled 7 1/2 weeks after the initial dose and every 4 weeks thereafter. After the third bleeding, the immunization program was discontinued for a three month period. Antigen booster injections were then resumed and the fourth bleeding was taken 10 days after immunization. Reasonable titers (that is, 50% binding of about 125 pg of tritium labeled Δ^8-THC at a final dilution of 1200-2700) were achieved in two out of four rabbits at the first bleeding. These titers compare quite favorably with those which have been reported by others and demonstrate that with this immunogen the rabbit is a reasonable animal to use for antiserum production.

The assay protocol is shown in Figure 5. Using this protocol, we measured the avidity of the antisera for various metabolites and analogs of Δ^9-THC by determining the relative amount of compound required for 50% displacement of initially bound radioligang. Although on theoretical grounds this procedure is not strictly valid, we have shown that in most instances it provides a useful guide to antibody selectivity (10).

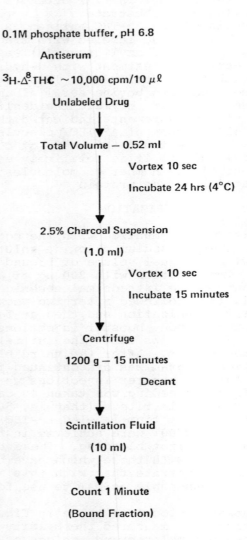

Figure 5.   General procedure for RIA of Δ⁹-THC

STRUCTURE BOUND	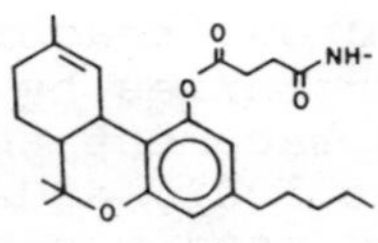 A	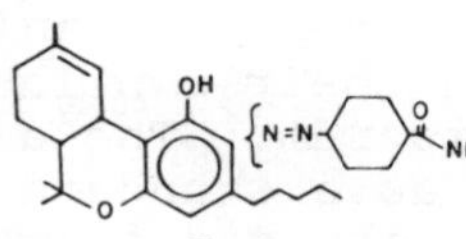 B	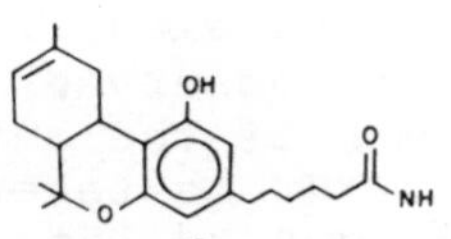 C
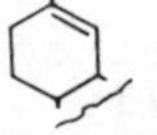 (Δ⁹)	100% (100)	100% (100)	100%
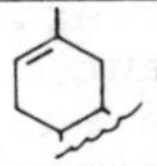 (Δ⁸)	63 (100)	48	271
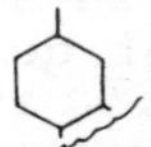 (HHC)	94	144	102
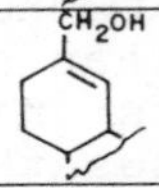 CH₂OH	244 (100)(as Δ⁸)	49 (47)	13
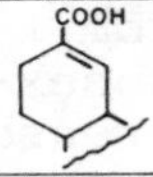 COOH	157 (<0.4)(as Δ⁸-COOMe)	2 (3)	0.6
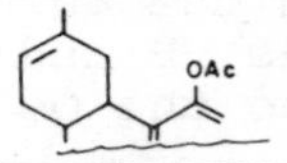 OAc	—	38	68
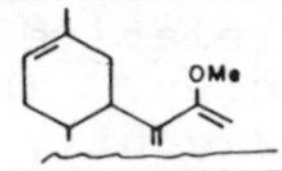 OMe	—	21	4
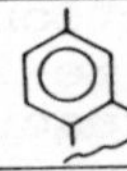 (CBN)	92	26	24
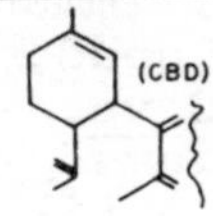 (CBD)	2	0.1 (0.5)	0.1

Figure 6. Structure-binding relationships of various antisera for cannabinoids

Through the National Institute on Drug Abuse and the courtesy of Drs. Gross and Marks, we were able to obtain samples of antisera prepared from three different immunogens, including our own, and to compare the cross reaction of these with various metabolites and analogs of tetrahydrocannabinol. This is shown in Figure 6. Since antibody selectivity can be significantly influenced by assay conditions, radioligand, etc.

Fig. 6 also lists the per cent cross reaction which has been observed in their own laboratories by the producers of the antiserum. The displacement ability of Δ^9-THC is taken as a standard at 100%, and for reasons discussed later, the radioligand used was tritium labeled Δ^8-THC with specific activity of about 50 Ci/mmole.

A change which alters the tricyclic character of the molecule, for example cannabidiol, essentially destroys binding to all of the antibodies. However, much more subtle changes can also have significant effects. In the case of antibody to Δ^8-THC, the shift of the double bond to the Δ^9-position results in a 2 1/2-fold decrease in cross-reaction. A similar decrease is seen on comparison of the binding of Δ^9- and Δ^8-THC to antibody obtained from the other two immunogens. Reduction of the cyclohexane double bond has no greater effect with the Δ^8-antibody than does the shift of the Δ^9-position and actually somewhat increases the cross-reaction with the Δ^9-Antiserum prepared from the azobenzoyl immunogen. Aromatization of the cyclohexene ring to cannabinol results in a fourfold decrease in cross-reaction as compared with Δ^9-THC in the case of the azobenzoyl- and amyl-linked immunogens, B and C, but has little effect on cross-reaction to the O-succinoyl antibody.

Oxygenated C-11 metabolites cross-react relatively little with the antibody from the amyl immunogen. The 11-hydroxy metabolite does cross-react significantly with the azobenzoyl antiserum, but the cross-reaction drops markedly when the 11-nor-9-carboxy metabolite is considered. Both of these metabolites do cross-react strongly with the antibody from the O-succinoyl immunogen A. The results shown indicated to us that good, although not outstanding selectivity for Δ^9-THC vs. a number of metabolites and analogs can be achieved with an amyl-linked immunogen and that useable antibody titers can be obtained in rabbits.

Δ^9-THC ANTISERUM

We therefore turned our attention to the preparation of an immunogen from 5'-carboxy-Δ^9-THC. The appropriate starting material was synthesized by Dr. Colin Pitt of our laboratory and the immunogen was synthesized as previously shown for the Δ^8-compound.

Again using the Δ^8-THC tritium labeled radioligand in the protocol described, we examined the 50% binding titer (initial dilution) of antisera from 16 rabbits.

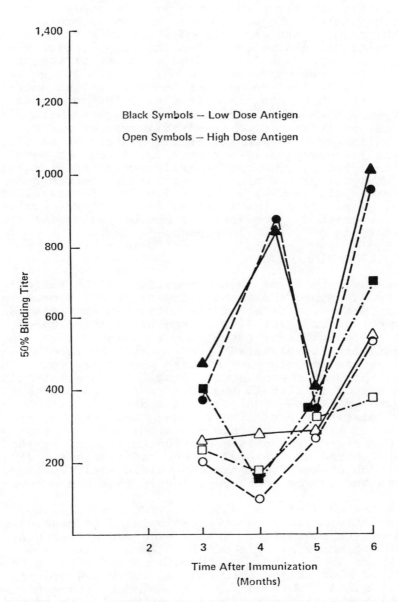

Figure 7.   *Antisera titers (initial dilution) for rabbits immunized with 200 μg (low dose, black symbols) or 500 μg (high dose, open symbols) of immunogen. Each symbol represents the average of two or three rabbits.*

The results are shown in Figure 7. The animals were
divided into six groups based on treatment protocol,
but the major factor in antibody titer was the dose of
immunogen. As can be seen from the figure, with the
exception of an unexplained drop in titer at the third
month the groups which were immunized with 200 µg of
immunogen exhibited rather consistently better antibody titers than those immunized with 500 µg.

Figure 8 shows standard curves generated with one
of these antisera. Good sensitivity was obtained.
This antiserum was used in the blind analysis of plasma
samples from marijuana smokers. These samples were
also analyzed by GC-MS at Battelle Institute. Regres-
sion analysis of the two sets of results showed good
agreement RIA (ng/ml) = 1.2 GC + 0.14 with excellent
correlation. Thus, the tritium labeled Δ^8-THC combined
with the antibody from the Δ^9-immunogen is useful for
the analysis of Δ^9-THC in plasma.

IODINATED RADIOLIGAND

Let us return now to a discussion of the radioligand used. Since the sensitivity of an RIA procedure
and the effective titer of the antiserum are related to
the specific radioactivity of the radioligand used,
there are significant advantages in using a high specific activity radiolabeled drug. A tritium labeled
drug has the advantage of binding properties very similar to those of the unlabeled drug. The greatest disadvantage of tritium is the fact that is is a β-emitter
analyzed by liquid scintillation techniques (which require relatively expensive reagents and form an in-
convenient step in attempts to automate RIA procedures).
For this reason there is a considerable trend at the
present to the use of ^{125}I as the radioisotope. It
has a much higher theoretical specific activity than
tritium and can be measured directly in a gamma counter.

In the case of analysis of Δ^9-THC not only must
the specific activity of the radioligand be considered,
but also its stability. When Δ^9-THC was prepared at
a specific activity of about 50 Ci/mmole, it had a
very short shelf life. On the other hand, tritiated
Δ^8-THC of similar specific radioactivity has proven
to be a quite stable entity. Its binding characteristics with the antisera raised to either Δ^8- or Δ^9-THC
make it a useful radioligand in spite of the heterolo-
gous nature of the assay thus introduced.

The advantages of ^{125}I enumerated before have led
us to also consider this substance as a radioisotope.

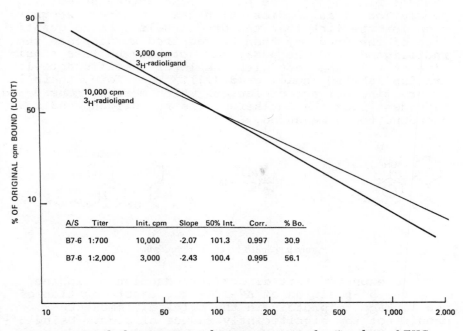

Figure 8. *Standard curves generated using antisera raised to 5'-carboxy-Δ⁹-THC-bovine serum albumin conjugate*

In most instances it has been found that, because of
its size, substitution of an iodine directly on a drug
molecule inhibits binding to the antibody. Therefore,
in many cases an iodohistamine or iodophenol derivative
has been linked to the derivative of the drug used for
the original immunogen preparation. However, this may
introduce other problems. The resulting substance may
have a structure in which the linkage between drug and
iodinated moiety is similar to that for the original
drug/protein conjugate. Thus, it may exhibit an increased binding vs. the parent drug or may select a
population of antibodies which has a greater recogni-
tion for the link than the drug itself. Large quantities of the drug may then be required to displace the
radioligand, and the assay may actually be less sensitive than is the case with the lower specific activity
tritium labeled radioligand (11). Therefore, there is
a very fine balance of factors which must be considered
dependent upon the antiserum, the radioligand and the
compound to be measured.

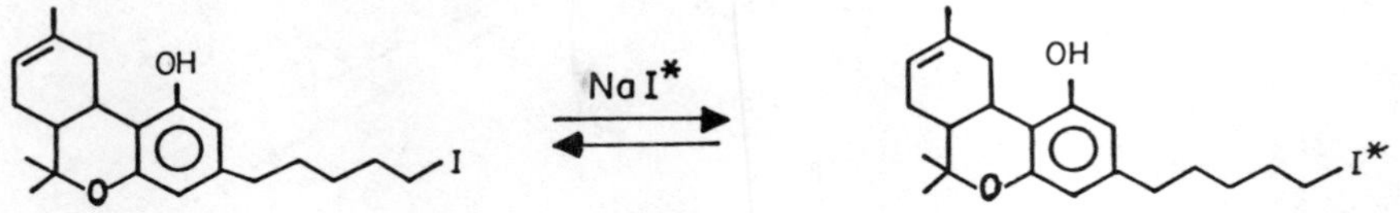

Figure 9.   Synthesis of ^{125}I radioligand

We expected that direct introduction of iodine
into the 5'-position of Δ^9-THC--the exact location of
the linkage to protein in the original immunogen--
should not too significantly reduce binding. Using 5'-
iodo-Δ^8-THC, we found that it exhibited 111% of the
binding of Δ^9-THC to the Δ^8-antibody. Dr. Pitt then
subjected 5'-iodo-Δ^8-THC to an exchange reaction using
$125I$ sodium iodide (Figure 9). Reaction at 50° led to
exchange as determined by ability to extract the radio-
iodine into hexane solution. Several batches of this
radioligand have now been prepared. The first had
relatively low specific activity, the second approximately 8-10 Ci/mmole. Standard curves utilizing this
iodinated material and the Δ^8-THC antiserum are shown
in Figure 10. When the lower activity material was
used, we obtained a standard curve with a 50% intercept
at about 1.2 ng/ml. Using the higher specific activity
iodinated radioligand, the second standard curve shown
was generated. It enabled us to obtain a sensitivity

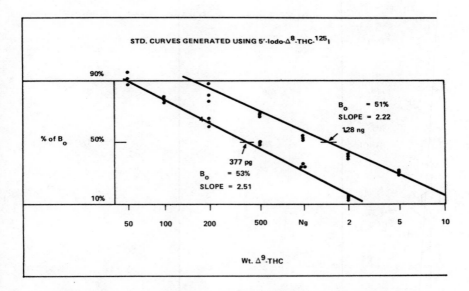

Figure 10.   Standard curves generated using 5'-iodo-Δ⁸-THC-¹²⁵I of varying specific activity

% CROSS REACTION WITH ANTISERUM TO

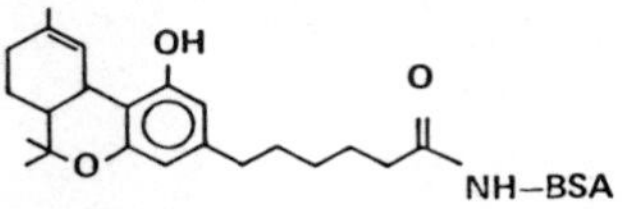

STRUCTURE BOUND	RADIOLIGAND USED	
	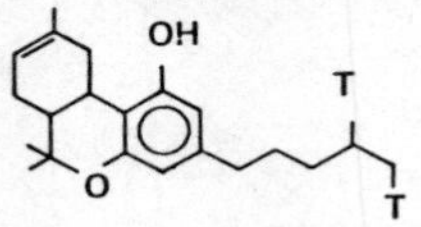	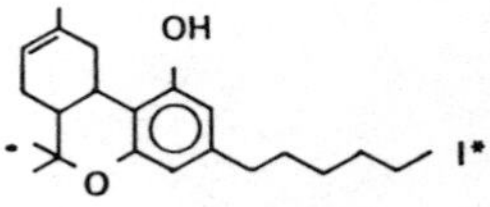
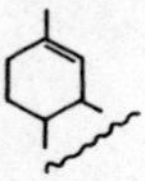 (Δ^9)	100%	100%
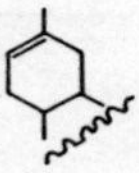 (Δ^8)	60	33
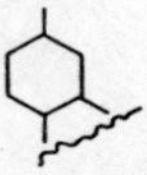 (HHC)	25	18
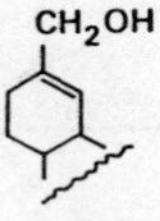	24	5.7
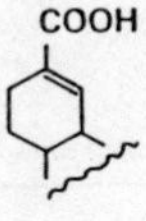	0.8	0.04
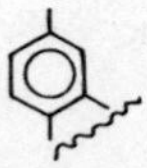 (CBN)	14	10
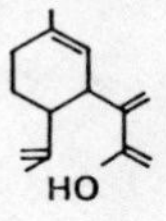 (CBD)	0.37	0.02

Figure 11. Comparison of cross reactivity to Δ^9-THC antiserum using tritiated and iodinated radioligands

of about 50 pg of Δ9-THC with a 50% intercept around
400 pg. We have also examined the use of the iodinated
radioligand with the antiserum prepared to 5'-carboxy-
Δ9-THC. The results of this are shown in Figure 11.
Here we compare initial data on cross reactions of antisera from the same rabbit using both the tritium and
iodine labeled material. In general, similar properties were observed. It thus appears that iodinated
material prepared in this manner may prove quite useful in radioimmunoassay of cannabinoid compounds. In
addition, we suggest that the approach used here may
prove generally useful in radioimmunoassay methodology,
for in principle many haptens can be converted in their
iodo derivatives and undergo the exchange procedure
used (12).

ACKNOWLEDGEMENTS

These studies were conducted under Contract No.
NO1-MH-1-0092 with the National Institute of Drug
Abuse, NIH.

REFERENCES

(1)   Landsteiner, K., "The Specificity of Serological
       Reactions", Dover Press, Inc., New York, 1962.
(2)   Wall, M. E., "Recent Advances in Phytochemistry",
       Ed., V. L. Runecktes, Vol. 9, Plenum, New York,
       1975, pp 29-59.
(3)   Cook, C. E., Hawes, M. L., Amerson, E. W.,
       Pitt, C. G. and Williams, D. L., "Cannabinoid
       Assay in Humans", National Institute on Drug
       Abuse Research Monograph Series 7, USDHEW, 1976,
       pp. 15-27.
(4)   Teale, J. D., Forman, E., King, L. J., and
       Marks, V., *Nature, 249,* 154 (1974).
(5)   Teale, J. D., Forman, E. J., King, L. J.,
       Piall, E. M. and Marks, V., *J. Pharm. Pharmac. 27,*
       465 (1975).
(6)   Tsui, P. T., Kelly, K. A., Ponpipom, M. M.,
       Strahilevitz, M., and Sehon, A. H., *Can. J. Bio-
       chem. 52,* 252 (1974).
(7)   Gross, S. J., Soares, J. R., Wong, S. L., and
       Schuster, R. E., *Nature, 252,* 581 (1974).
(8)   Pitt, C. G., Hobbs, P. T., Schran, H., Twine,
       C. E., Jr., and Williams, D. L., *J. Label. Comp.
       11,* 551 (1975).
(9)   Vaitukaitis, J., Robbins, J. B., Nieschlag, E.,
       and Ross, G. E., *J. Clin. Endocrinol 33,* 988,
       (1971).

(10) Cook, C. E., Tallent, C. R., Amerson, E. W.,
     Myers, M. W., Kepler, J. A., Taylor, G. F., and
     Christensen, H. D., *J. Pharmacol. Exp. Therap.*
     199, 679 (1976).
(11) Hunter, W. M., Lars, P. W. and Rutherford, F. J.
     in "Steroid Immunoassay", Eds. E. D. H. Cameron,
     S. G. Hillier and K. Griffiths, Alpha Omega
     Publishing Ltd., Cardiff, Wales, U. K., 1975,
     pp. 141-152.
(12) Cook, C. E., Hawes, M. L., Amerson, E. W.,
     Pitt, C. G., Williams, D. L., and Willette,
     R. G., *Pharmacologist 18*, 291 (1976).
(13) Cook, C. E., Christensen, H. D., Amerson, E. W.,
     Kepler, J. A., Tallent, C. R., and Taylor, G. F.,
     "Radioimmunoassay of Anticonvulsant Drugs:
     Phenytoin, Phenobarbital, and Primidone," in
     Quantitative Analytic Studies in Epilepsy,
     Kellaway, P. and Petersen, I., Eds.; Raven
     Press: New York, 1976; p. 40.

RECEIVED January 2, 1979.

Antisera Raised Against Tetrahydrocannabinol in the Radioimmunoassay of Cannabinoids

J. D. TEALE, JACQUELINE M. CLOUGH, L. J. KING, and V. MARKS

Department of Biochemistry, University of Surrey, Guildford, Surrey, United Kingdom

P. L. WILLIAMS and A. C. MOFFAT

Home Office Central Research Establishment, Aldermaston, Berkshire, United Kingdom

Radioimmunoassay (RIA), whether it is used for the measurement of peptides, steroids or drugs, has many attractions, particularly for the routine laboratory engaged in the analysis of large numbers of samples. The major attribute of RIA is its potential for the detection of picogram quantities of compound, often by direct analysis of untreated biological specimens. In the measurement of low molecular weight substances, such as drugs, RIA can provide results on many samples in a matter of hours. The use of automated procedures will increase the speed of operation still further, as well as improving precision. The original RIA concept (1) was based on antibodies to a naturally immunogenic peptide (insulin) but it is possible to produce antibodies to any non-protein molecule by attachment to an immunogenic carrier molecule (2). Attention has turned recently to the development of RIA for drugs (3), particularly those drugs given in low doses and requiring a sensitive detection system.

Considerable progress has been made over the past decade in the measurement of drugs by RIA. The main reason for the advance in this application of the technique is the improved development of the key reagents; antiserum and radioactive label. More effective meth-

0-8412-0488-8/79/47-098-155$05.00/0

© 1979 American Chemical Society

ods have lead to the production of higher specific
activity tritiated drugs, with a concommitant increase
in assay sensitivity. Liquid scintillation counting
is used for counting tritium. This type of labeling
provides a tracer with similar antibody-combining
properties to the native drug and obviates problems
often encountered with iodinated drug derivative, for
example (4).

Antiserum properties exert the greatest influence
on assay performance, both in terms of sensitivity and
specificity. It is usual to aim for a high avidity;
monospecific antibody present in the serum at high
titre. Such antibodies will bind antigen tightly resulting in (1) shorter incubation times, (2) minimal
disturbance in antigen-antibody binding during phase
separation of free and antibody-bound fractions of
antigen, and (3) the sensitive displacement of tracer
with standard preparations. A high titre antiserum
although not essential, permits the establishment of
assay conditions and analysis of large numbers of specimens using the same reagents. The problem of antiserum specificity - the ability to bind a single compound in the presence of many others - remains as yet
the unsolved mystery of RIA. Specificity can be influenced through the point of attachment of the antigen to carrier protein during immunogen production.
Then, following Landsteiner's hypothesis (5), the antibodies produced following immunization with such a
conjugate will recognize that part of the antigen fur-
thest from its link to the carrier. However, even
after strenuous efforts to produce a conjugate designed
to elicit specific antibodies, genetic variation within the groups of animals immunized still makes the
result uncertain.

Antibody Production

Attempts to produce antisera for use in the specific measurement of THC by RIA (6-9) provide an example
of the inconsistencies in the induction of antibodies
to small molecules. At the University of Surrey several different THC-protein conjugates have been produced using reactions involving the phenolic hydroxyl
group of THC. Figure 1 lists the products formed.
Rabbits and sheep were immunized with these conjugates.
None of the rabbits produced antibodies which bound
^{3}H-THC, but some sera did exhibit binding of radio-
iodinated THC-copolymer. This copolymer is shown in
Figure 2. This binding was not inhibited by standard
THC but could be decreased with unlabeled THC-polymer.

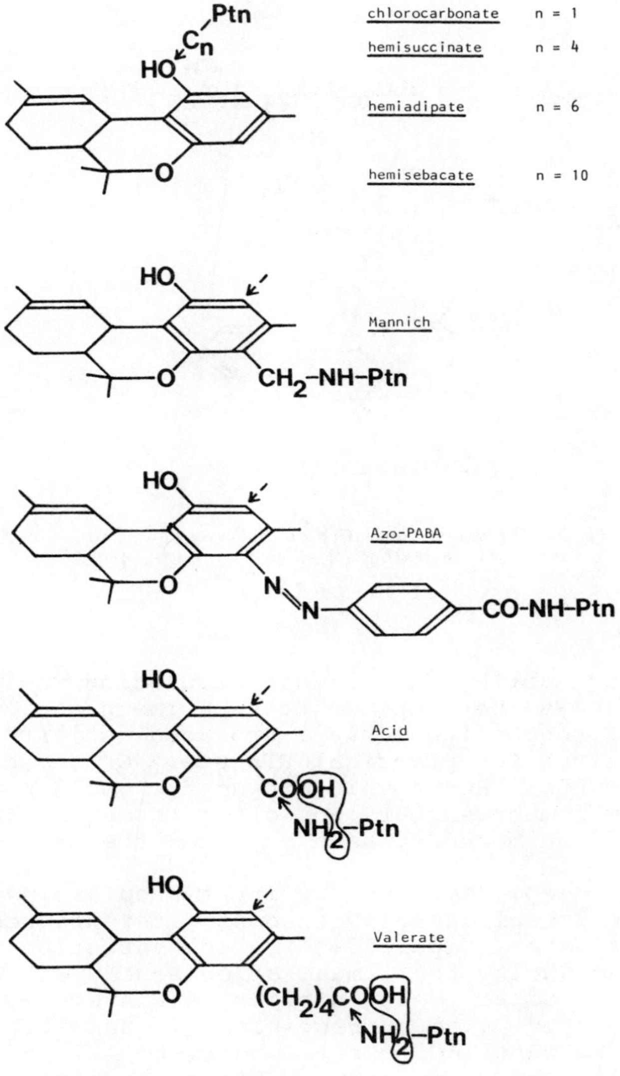

Figure 1. *Conjugation reactions used in the production of THC-bovine serum albumin conjugates. Ptn is the symbol for the protein.*

It would seem that rabbit antisera contained antibodies capable of recognizing only THC derivatized at the hydroxyl.

The same conjugates, when injected into sheep,

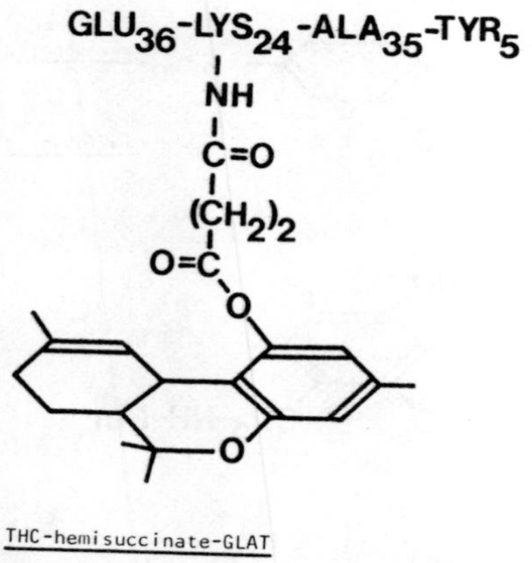

$$GLU_{36}-LYS_{24}-ALA_{35}-TYR_{5}$$

THC-hemisuccinate-GLAT

Figure 2. The hemisuccinate derivative of THC conjugated to a synthetic poly-
mer (MW 30,000) of GLAT in the ratio 36:24:35:5

did produce antibodies capable of binding ^{3}H-THC.
Table 1 shows the response to each immunogen. Of the
7 animals responding, only 2 produced antisera of sufficient titre for practical RIA use. On the basis of
these results, THC-protein conjugates would appear to
be of low immunogenicity and other research groups,
using similar methods, have reported the same conclusions.

One sheep, immunized by intramuscular injection
of THC-hemisuccinate-albumin conjugate, produced our
assay antisera. Figure 3 shows the variation in antibody titre during the immunization schedule. Using
sera collected at peaks in titre, a RIA system has
been developed. The current assay is sensitive to
50 picogram pure THC, corresponding to 1.5 ng/ml in
plasma and 1 ng/ml in urine. Figure 4 shows a typical
standard curve correlating the percentage of ^{3}H-THC
antibody-bound with the presence of increasing amounts
of pure THC. Assay methodology has been published in
detail (10).

Although raised against THC, the assay antiserum
is not specific for that compound, but binds several
cannabinoids to varying degrees. An example of the
unpredictable nature of antiserum specificity is demon-

TABLE 1

Conjugate Immunogenicity in Sheep

THC Derivative Conjugated to BSA	Number Responding / Number Immunized
Chlorocarbonate (1C link through hydroxyl)	2/3
Hemisuccinate (4C link through hydroxyl)	4/10
Hemiadipate (6C link through hydroxyl)	1/3
Hemisebacate (10C link through hydroxyl)	0/5
Azo-PABA (Phenyl link para to hydroxyl)	0/5
Mannich (1C link para to hydroxyl)	0/1
Acid (1C link para to hydroxyl)	0/2
Valerate (5C link para to hydroxyl)	0/2
Total	7/29 (24%)

strated by Tables 2 and 3. Table 2 shows a comparison of the cross-reactivity patterns of two antisera. Antiserum 133Y/30/9 was produced by us and R41/11 by Prof. M. Cais, Department of Chemistry, Technion Institute of Technology, Haifa, Israel. R41/11 was raised in a rabbit against Δ^8-THC-11-oic acid conjugated to BSA and is of high titre. (This demonstrates that it is possible to produce THC antibodies relatively easily and in smaller animal species). However, in spite of the use of different conjugates given to different animal species, the cross-reactivity patterns are almost identical. Plasma samples from a cancer patient under therapeutic THC treatment, were assayed with the two antisera and similar results were obtained (Table 3). Assay of urine specimens from the same patient, however, indicated lower levels (approximately half) with R41/11.

From the results of the different research groups

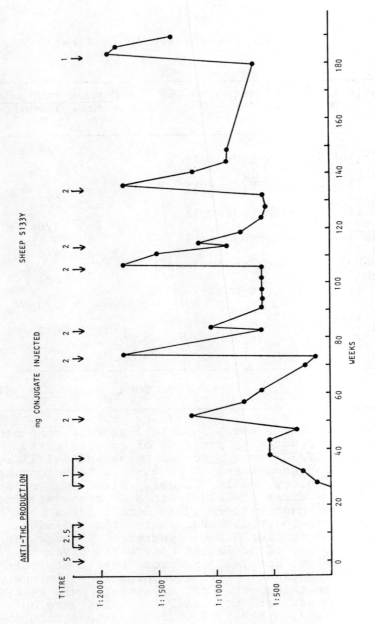

Figure 3.   Immunization schedule and antibody titre in a sheep injected intramuscularly with THC-hemisuccinate-BSA in the amounts shown. Titre is defined as the reciprocal of the dilution of antiserum that bound 50% of the ³H-THC label.

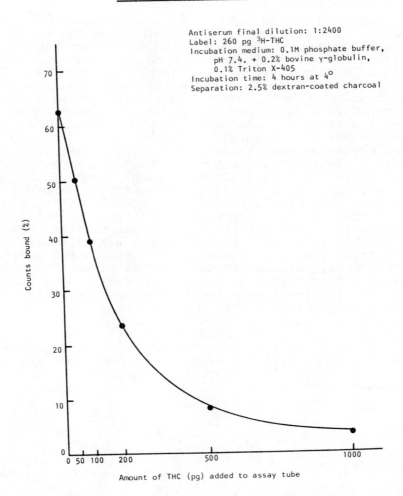

ASSAY STANDARD CURVE FOR THC

Antiserum final dilution: 1:2400
Label: 260 pg ³H-THC
Incubation medium: 0.1M phosphate buffer,
    pH 7.4. + 0.2% bovine γ-globulin,
    0.1% Triton X-405
Incubation time: 4 hours at 4°
Separation: 2.5% dextran-coated charcoal

Figure 4. Standard curve constructed using the conditions shown. Displacement of ³H-THC from antibody binding sites by increasing amounts of THC in assay buffer is measured.

throughout the world, therefore, information has accumulated on the immunogenic properties of various THC-protein conjugates. While antibody production to THC can now be virtually guarenteed, the specificity of the product almost certainly will not be restricted to THC.

Applications of RIA

Although our RIA system is not THC-specific, it is specific for the 3-ringed cannabinoid nucleus and can be used as a sensitive and rapid cannabinoid detection system. This RIA system has been used for the measurement of THC cross-reacting cannabinoid (THC-CRC) levels in 1002 urine specimens collected from various sources. For this purpose the cross-reactivity with metabolites is beneficial since THC is not excreted unchanged (11). Figure 5 shows the number of samples from each source and the percentage positive in each group. The 82 control specimens were taken from hospital in-patients for routine biochemical analyses. The 740 samples received for routine drug analysis at a local hospital during the periods December 1974 to February 1975 and May 1975 and July 1975 were screened for THC-CRC. These samples originated from two hospital addiction treatment clinics (A and B) and two independent treatment centers (C and hostel). Also included were miscellaneous specimens from other sources, such as general medical departments, psychiatric clinics and general practitioners' surgeries. In addition 172 specimens taken from new detainees at a juvenile detention center (subjects arriving directly from home).

TABLE 2
Cross-reactivities of pure cannabinoids with two antisera raised against different THC-protein conjugates in different species.

Antiserum	133Y/30/9	R41/11
Species	Sheep	Rabbit
Immunogen	$(Ptn)NH-CO-(CH_2)_2-C \overset{O}{\underset{}{}}$ ... C_5H_{11}	$\theta=C$ NH(Ptn) OH ... C_5H_{11}
Final titre	1:2400	1:18000
Cannabinoid	% cross-reactivity	
Δ^9-THC	100	100
11-hydroxy-Δ^9-THC	160	100
8,11-dihydroxy-Δ^9-THC	150	200
11-carbomethoxy-Δ^8-THC	46	54
11-carboxy-Δ^8-THC methyl ether	1.4	6.4
Cannabinol	66	40
11-hydroxy-cannabinol	6.3	3.2
Cannabidiol	3.2	2.0

TABLE 3

THC-CRC levels in plasma and urine specimens from a cancer patient undergoing therapeutic treatment with THC. Levels were measured using the two antisera described in Table 2.

Plasma samples	THC-CRC (ng/ml)	
	133Y/30/9	R41/11
1	0	0
2	176	192
3	204	196
4	320	316
5	220	228
6	296	304
7	164	174
8	160	188
Urine samples		
1	96	56
2	492	240
3	472	304

Figure 5 shows that none of the control specimens contained cannabinoids. Approximately 30% of specimens from hospital treatment clinics were positive for THC-CRC, while 50-60% of the samples from independent centers were positive. The incidence of positive specimens in the miscellaneous group was lower (13%). Only 3 of the 172 detention center samples contained THC-CRC and each inmate admitted subsequently to having smoked cannabis in the 48 hours prior to his arrival at the detention center.

The 740 specimens received for routine drug analysis were divided into groups according to the level of THC-CRC detected. Figure 6 shows the data pattern. Values of 10 µg/l or less were classed as negative. 35% of the specimens were positive and half of these contained very high levels.

The assay was also used for the measurement of THC-CRC levels in plasma and 24-hour urine specimens collected following the smoking of a cigarette impregnated with 5 mg pure THC by each of 4 volunteers (12). Figure 7 shows the plasma levels detected in each of the volunteers. As a comparison the plasma THC level in a car driver fatally injured in a traffic accident (13) was measured. The driver's plasma level of

350 µg/l can be compared with a peak value of 70 µg/l in one volunteer immediately after smoking when sub-jective feelings of mild euphoria were reported. Fig-ure 8 shows the urinary THC-CRC levels in the volun-teers. The driver was found to have a urinary level of 1215 µg/l.

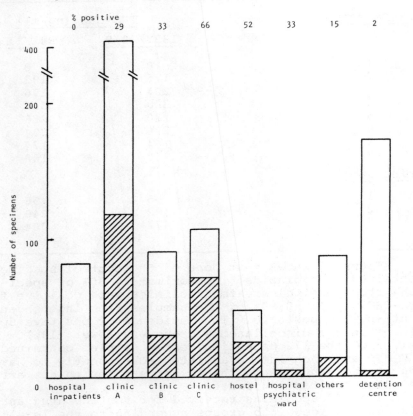

Figure 5.   Proportion of urine samples positive for THC–CRC according to the origin of the sample. Hatched areas indicate positive THC–CRC specimens.

The screening of post mortem specimens from other fatally injured drivers, following the original case, was undertaken with the cooperation of coroners and pathologists throughout England and Wales. Between July 1976 and December 1976 blood samples from 50 cases were received, 40 involving car drivers and 10 motor-cyclists. The upper part of Figure 9 shows the speci-mens grouped according to the victim's age, and in the

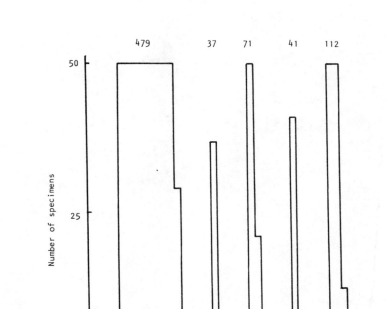

Figure 6. *THC–CRC in 740 urine specimens received for routine drug analysis from patients known or suspected to be taking drugs*

lower part of the diagram the specimens have been grouped according to the regional source. It will be noted that 70% of the specimens came from subjects under 30 years of age and that nearly half came from one area of England. The samples were received from a total of 24 different pathologists. The THC-CRC levels in the 5 positive cases (2 of them being motorcyclists) fell within a moderate 25-65 μg/l range, which could not be considered to have exerted the same degree of intoxication and, therefore, influence on driving capability as the very high levels observed in the original case. The group of specimens analyzed cannot be considered representative for several reasons, because only 7 cases were received from the most highly populated area - the South East of England. However, the study constitutes an example of RIA use in epidemiological studies.

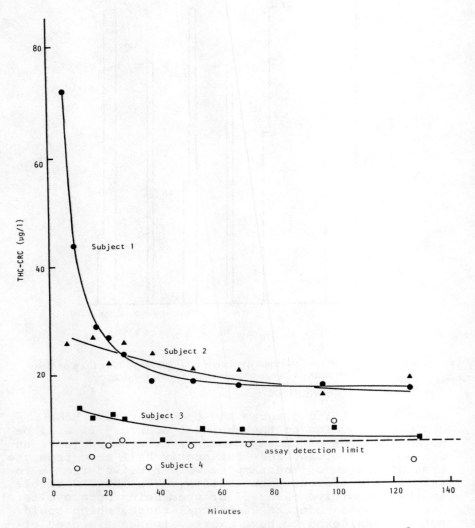

Figure 7. Plasma THC–CRC in four healthy volunteers who began smoking a cigarette impregnated with 5 mg THC at zero time. Subjects 1 and 2 were cigarette smokers; subject 3, a cigar smoker; and subject 4, a pipe smoker. The level detected in a post morten specimen from a car driver was 350 µg/L.

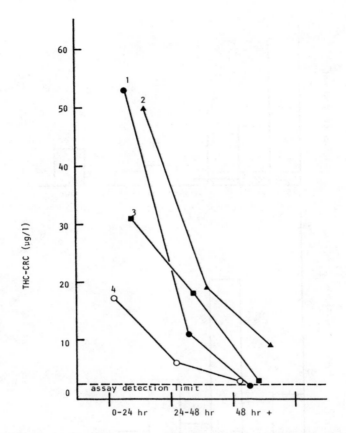

Figure 8. Urinary THC–CRC in the same subjects described in Figure 7

High Pressure Liquid Chromatography (HPLC) and RIA

Work has recently been undertaken at the Home Office Central Research Establishment at Aldermaston on a procedure for the specific measurement of THC and its metabolites. Following an initial HPLC separation stage, the RIA is used as a sensitive quantatative method for screening column eluants. HPLC separation was performed on a reverse phase column system - highly polar compounds being eluted first followed by substances of decreasing polarity. Methanol extracts of plasma or hydrolyzed urine samples were chromatographed.

Figure 10 shows chromatograms of a sample of urine collected from a rabbit following an intravenous dose of 100 μg ^{14}C-THC. The urine was subjected to

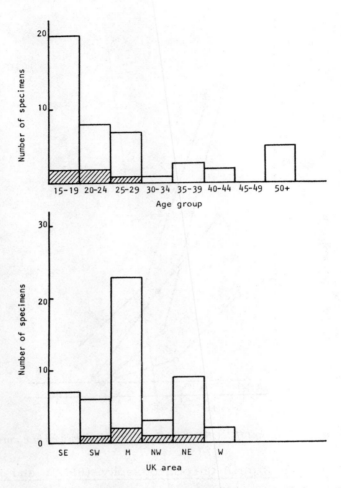

Figure 9. Post mortem blood specimens from 50 drivers, received during July 1976–December 1976 and 24 centers. (Upper) Specimens grouped according to the victims age. (Lower) Specimens grouped according to regional source. (SE = South East England; SW = South West; M = Midlands; NW = North West; NE = North East; W = Wales). Hatched areas represent specimens positive for THC–CRC.

alkaline hydrolysis before separation since cannabinoid compounds from untreated urine were eluted in a single peak concurrently with highly polar material. In the diagram, the plain line represents the amount of radio-activity in the column eluent due to ^{14}C-labeled canna-

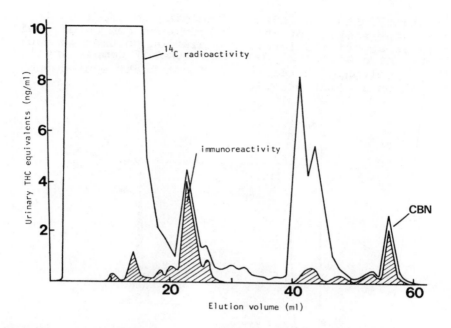

Figure 10. Radiochromatogram and radioimmunochromatogram of THC metabolites in hydrolyzed rabbit urine. Urine was collected following an iv dose of 100 μg ¹⁴C-THC. Fractions collected from HPLC separation of hydrolyzed urine were screened for ¹⁴C radioactivity (plain lines) and THC–CRC (hatched peaks). The elution volume for pure CBN is indicated.

binoids. The hatched peaks represent THC-CRC levels measured by the RIA. The last peak of cannabinoids eluted coincided with the elution volume of pure cannabinol.

THC and cross-reacting metabolites were measured in extracts of plasma samples taken from a volunteer at timed intervals after smoking 10 mg pure THC. Figure 11 shows the peaks of THC-CRC measured in plasma samples taken before smoking and at 2, 12, 24 and 34 minutes after smoking. The control plasma specimen is seen to contain residual cannabinoids of high polarity and these are probably due to the previous use of cannabis by the volunteer which was only revealed after the results shown were obtained. In the samples taken after smoking, THC can be seen to decrease progressively and metabolites of various polarities increase and decrease over the time of sampling. The peak of high polarity compounds remained relatively

constant. Also included in the diagram are the elution
points of samples of the few reference compounds available in a purified form. The elution volumes in each
case were uncorrected for the volume of sample applied
to the column. Therefore the first peaks eluted show
variation in elution volume.

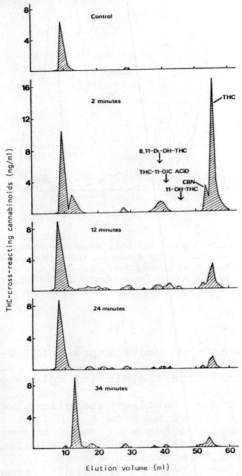

*Figure 11. Radioimmunochromatograms of plasma samples taken from a volun-
teer before, and 2, 12, 24, and 34 min after smoking 10 mg THC. Sample extracts
of 1.5–6.0 mL were injected and the elution volumes are uncorrected.*

A urine specimen, collected from the same volunteer 60 minutes after smoking, was subjected to alka-

line hydrolysis. The hydrolysate was chromatographed under different column conditions to those used for the plasma analyses. Figure 12 shows the resultant radio-immunochromatogram with mainly 2 peaks of THC-CRC, the second peak being eluted at the elution volume of pure cannabinol.

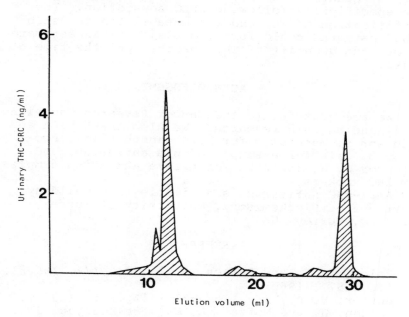

Figure 12. Radioimmunochromatogram of a urine sample taken from a volunteer 60 min after smoking 10 mg THC. The urine was hydrolyzed before HPLC separation. The elution volume for CBN was 29 mL.

The nature of most of the compounds separated from these samples is unknown and this emphasizes the advantage of a broad specificity antiserum in the detection of urinary THC metabolites. Indeed, none of the metabolites (11-hydroxy-THC, 8,11-dihydroxy-THC and THC-11-oic acid) known to cross-react with the RIA antiserum, are seen to be present in the hydrolyzed urine sample (Figure 12). These compounds as shown in Figure 11 have elution volumes greater than 40 ml. On the basis of these results an RIA specific for these compounds would not have found any detectable material in the urine. To develop the combination of HPLC and RIA further, an antiserum exhibiting complete cross-reactivity with all metabolites would be of greatest benefit.

In summary, RIA has two applications in the screening of plasma and urine specimens for cannabis use. Direct analysis of a sample gives an indication of the presence of cannabinoids on a semi-quantitative basis. Quantitation may then be expanded further and more specifically following HPLC separation. The identification of THC and its metabolites in established patterns could form the basis for an estimate of both the quantity of THC absorbed and the time of intake.

ACKNOWLEDGEMENTS

We are grateful to the Cancer Research Campaign for financing this research. We also thank NIDA and Professor R. Mechoulam for pure cannabinoids, Professor M. Cais for a sample of his antiserum, and Professor J. W. Thompson for plasma and urine samples from THC smokers.

Anti-THC antiserum is available from Guildhay, Department of Biochemistry, University of Surrey, Guildford, Surrey, UK.

REFERENCES

(1) Yalow, R. S. and Berson, S. A., *J. Clin. Invest.*
     39, 1157 (1960).
(2) Butler, V. P., *Adv. Immunol. 17*, 255 (1973).
(3) Landon, J. and Moffat, A. C., *The Analyst 101*,
     225 (1976).
(4) Robinson, J. D., et. al. "Radioimmunoassay in
     Clinical. Biochemistry", Ed., C. Pasternak, London
     Press, Heyden, 1975, p. 113.
(5) Landsteiner, K., "The Specificity of Serological
     Reactions", Dover Press, New York, 1962.
(6) Gross, S. J., Soares, J. R., Wong, S-L.R. and
     Schuster, R. E., *Nature 252*, 581 (1974).
(7) Tsui, P. T., Kelly, K. A., Ponpipom, M. M.,
     Strahilevitz, M. and Sehon, A. H., *Can. J. Biochem. 52*, 252 (1974).
(8) Van Vunakis, H. and Levine, L., "Immunoassays
     for Drugs Subject to Abuse", S. J. Mule,
     I. Sunshine, M. Braude and R. E. Willette, Eds.,
     CRC Press, Cleveland, Ohio, 1974, p. 23.
(9) Cais, M., Dani, S., Josephy, Y., Modiano, A.,
     Gershon, H. and Mechoulam, R., *FEBS Letters 55*,
     257 (1975).
(10) Teale, J. D., Forman, E. J., King, L. J.,
     Piall, E. M. and Marks, V., *J. Pharm. Pharmac. 27*,
     465 (1975).

(11)   Hollister, L. E., Kanter, S. L. Board, R. D.
       and Green, D. E., *Res. Commun. Chem. Path.*
       Pharmac. *8,* 579 (1974).
(12)   Teale, J. D., Forman, E. J., King, L. J. and
       Marks, V., *Lancet,* ii, 553 (1974).
(13)   Teale, J. D. and Marks, V., *Lancet,* i, 884
       (1976).

RECEIVED December 12, 1978.

HPLC Analyses of Δ^9-Tetrahydrocannabinol and 11-Nor-Δ^9-tetrahydrocannabinol-9-carboxylic Acid in Human Plasma

JIMMIE L. VALENTINE[1], OWEN H. M. GAN, H. C. NIO, and EVERETT D. THOMPSON

School of Pharmacy, Bio-Analytics Laboratory, University of Missouri—Kansas City, Kansas City, MO 64108

Detection of marijuana use in humans has been a pressing need for law enforcement officials as well as forensic scientists. Work performed in our laboratories has centered principally around finding suitable techniques for identifying prior use of marijuana by analysis of various body fluids following marijuana smoking. A guiding axiom in initiation of this work was previous findings that Δ^9-tetrahydrocannabinol produced the psychotomimetic effects (2) as well as some of the observed physiological responses (3) following marijuana smoking. Marijuana contains four constituents of similar structure: Δ^9-tetrahydrocannabinol (I); cannabidiol (II); cannabinol (III); and cannabichrome (IV) which appear in varying quantities depending upon the geographic origin of the marijuana plant (4). Thus human body fluids would most likely contain these constituents as well as possible metabolites of each.

[1] Current address: Dept. of Pharmacology, Schools of Medicine and Dentistry, Oral Roberts University, Tulsa, OK 74171.

0-8412-0488-8/79/47-098-175$07.75/0

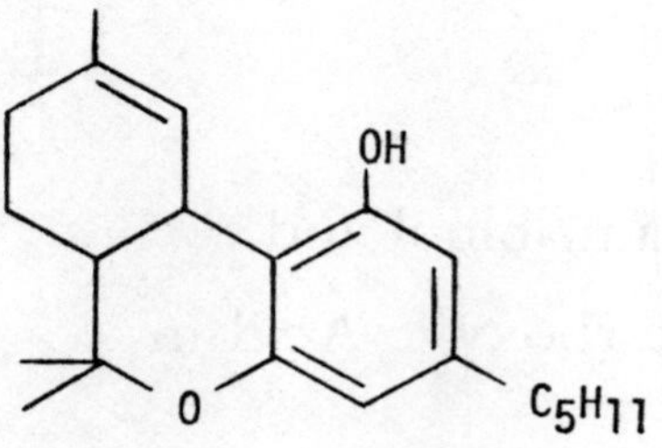

I

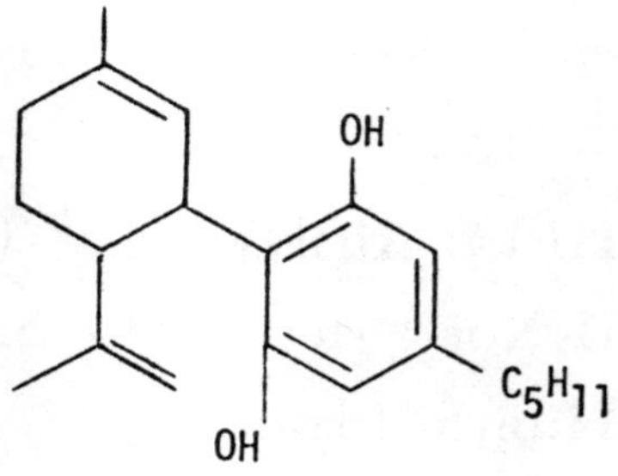

II

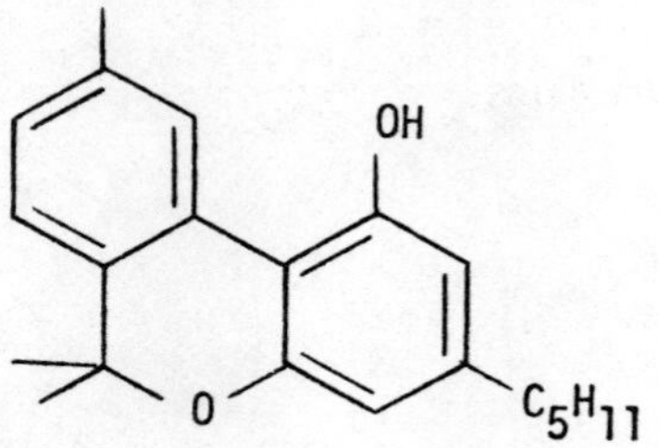

III

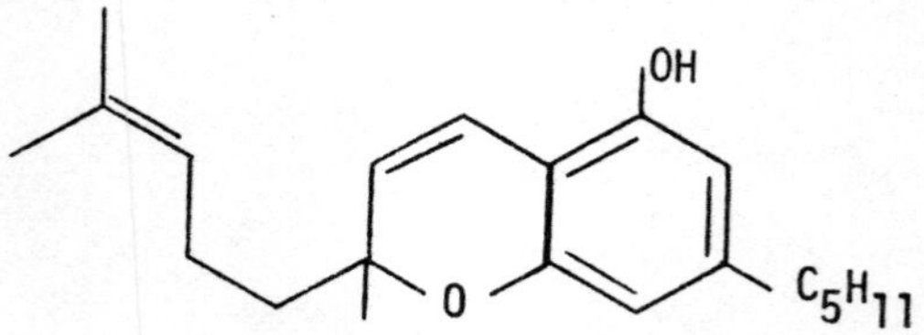

IV

Metabolism of I in humans has been studied by several groups (5-8) with findings that 11-hydroxy-Δ^9-tetrahydrocannabinol (V) and 11-nor-Δ^9-tetrahydrocanni-binol-9-carboxylic acid (VI) are the principal metabolites.

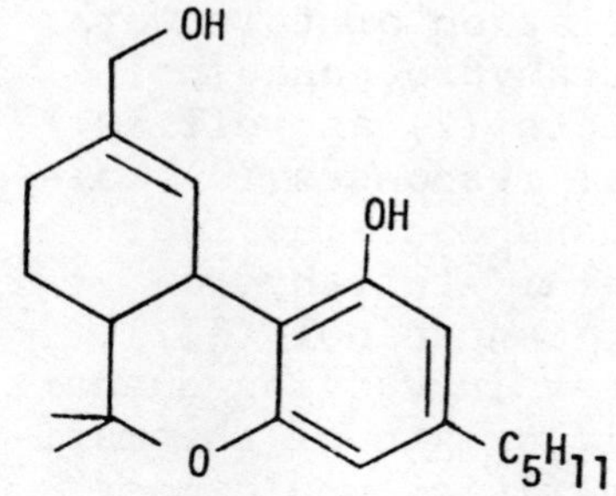

V

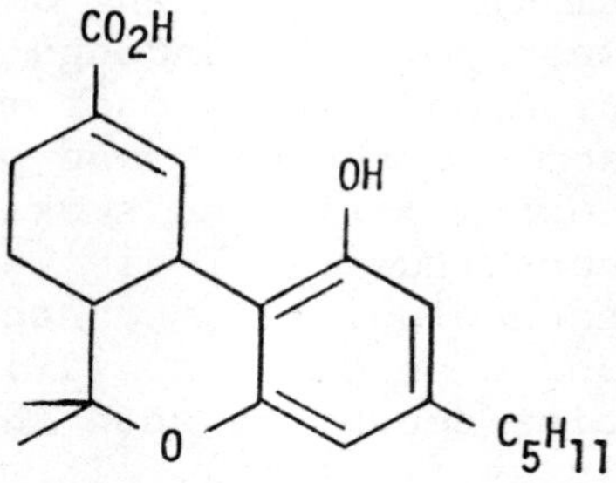

VI

These findings also indicated a need to have an analytical technique for identifying V and/or VI in body fluids as evidence that I had been present.

As the analytical technique for the assay work done in our laboratories, high pressure liquid chromatography (HPLC) was chosen. HPLC was chosen as the

primary separatory technique based upon three reasons:
1) speed of analysis, 2) no need for derivatization,
and 3) destructive pyrolytic conditions were not required. The latter point was felt to be particularly
pertinent since Kephalas and co-workers (9) had found
that pyrolysis of II via smoking yielded I, III and
Δ^9-tetrahydrocannabinol.

In the present chapter a presentation will be made
of the various HPLC assay techniques employed in our
laboratory for assaying I and VI in human plasma with a
discussion of parameters attempted and methods developed.

HPLC ASSAY METHODS

As discussed above, marijuana contains four constituents (viz,I-IV) similar in structure and chemical
properties whereas the metabolites are more polar and
in the case of V and VI, more acidic than I. Thus it
seemed plausible that I-IV could be separated from V
and VI in plasma based upon pH adjustment and solvent
extraction properties. Compounds I-IV were found to be
extractable at ambient pH of 7.4 using petroleum ether
whereas V and VI could be extracted at pH 4.1 using
99:1, benzene:isopropanol. Once the initial plasma
separation was effected a chromatographic separation
was feasible using normal phase conditions for I-IV and
reverse phase conditions for V and VI. Each technique
is detailed in the following sections.

NORMAL PHASE HPLC

The major goals in developing a satisfactory normal phase HPLC method for I-IV in plasma were adequate
resolution from each other and endogenous plasma constituents, as well as finding a detection method capable of providing the required sensitivity. Figure 1
illustrates the first successful method devised in our
laboratory for separating the major cannabinoids when
present in human plasma. The separation technique
employed a gradient elution program using heptane and
methylene chloride on a silica gel column. The gradient started at 5% methylene chloride in heptane and
proceeded to 95% methylene chloride over a 9 minute
period. The program was reversed, i.e., from 5:95%
to the initial 95:5% heptane-methylene chloride mixture, thereby regenerating the column. A solvent flow
rate of 120 ml/hr. was used to obtain optimum resolution of the individual cannabinoids. Detection was
accomplished using a spectrophotometer set at 273.7 nm.

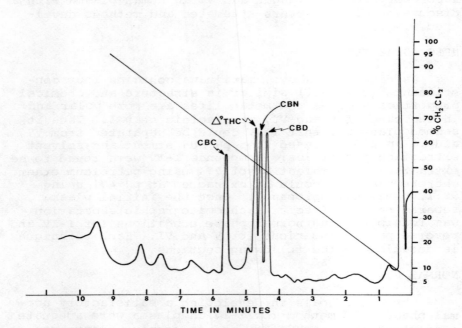

Figure 1.   HPLC analysis of 1 mL human plasma from non-marijuana smokers to which 1.0 μg of II (CBD), 0.25 μg of III (CBN), 1.0 μg of I (Δ⁹-THC), and 0.25 μg of IV (CBC) were added. A gradient program (solid superimposed line) was used starting with 95:5, heptane:methylene chloride.

This wavelength was shown to be the point of maximum absorption for I using stop flow conditions and UV scanning as I eluted from the silica gel column. The other cannabinoids (i.e., II-IV) were somewhat less responsive at this wavelength.

As noted in Figure 1, 1.0 µg of I in 1 ml of human plasma gave a readily detectable signal. Subsequent work demonstrated that 100 ng/ml of I was detectable but not quantifiable in a reproducible manner. Since other workers (3,10-12) had previously shown human plasma levels of I to be less than 100 ng/ml shortly after marijuana smoking, it was obvious that a wavelength of 273.7 nm was less than satisfactory for the required sensitivity.

As one solution to the needed sensitivity, mass spectrometry (MS) was used. This previously described technique (13) utilized a trideuterated isotope of I (d_3-I) as the internal standard. Since both I and d_3-I eluted from the HPLC column simultaneously it was possible to detect their presence at 273.7 nm as a result of 1.6 µg/ml of d_3-I having been added to each sample. Collection of the fraction containing both I and d_3-I as it eluted from the HPLC column was followed by MS quantification using an alternating ion event counting technique (13,14). Use of this technique on plasma from eleven marijuana smokers gave results which were comparable to other workers findings (3,10-12) and the average plasma level curve thus obtained is given in Figure 2.

Although the HPLC-MS method was demonstrated to be accurate and precise, as well as specific for I in plasma, the method was not amenable to low sample cost or rapidity of processing. For example, approximately two hours were required to process one sample at a cost of $80.00 per sample. These facts prompted a search for a more expedient and less expensive assay method.

An earlier study on the ultraviolet absorption properties of the cannabinoids performed in our laboratory gave reason to predict that HPLC-UV analysis of these compounds might be feasible. As shown in Figure 3, this reassessment of ultraviolet spectral properties of I-IV clearly demonstrated a preponderance of absorption characteristics of I at 212 nm as contrasted to 273.7 nm used in our earlier work. Literature values had been reported for absorption patterns of I (15), II (16), III (16), and IV (17) at higher wavelengths but not in the region of 200-240 nm. Exact determinations of extinction coefficients for these compounds in methyl alcohol as given in Table I, exemplify these properties. Since, as was discussed above, 100 ng/ml

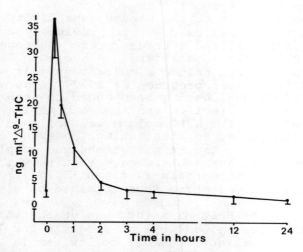

Figure 2. Average plasma level of I found in 11 human male subjects following smoking of a marijuana cigarette containing 10.8 mg of I. Vertical bars below each data point indicate the standard deviation for the set at each time interval.

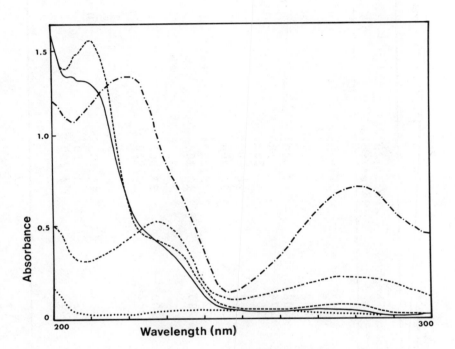

Figure 3.   UV-absorption curves for the major cannabinoids: (– – –), I (Δ^9-THC); (——), II (CBD); (– · –), III (CBN); (– – · – –), IV (CBC); (· · ·), methyl alcohol used as solvent.

TABLE 1

Molar Absorbtivity of Some Cannabinoids in Methanol

Compound	Wavelength (nm)	Molar Absorbtivity (liter/mole · cm)	Concentration
Δ^9-tetrahydrocan- nabinol (I)	209 275 283	52,470 1,760 1,810	10 mg/ml
cannabidiol (II)	208.5 274 281	9,000 218 222	50 mg/ml
cannabinol (III)	222 285	45,970 24,800	10/mg/ml
cannabichrome (IV)	229 280	28,300 10,100	10 mg/ml
11-hydroxy-Δ^9-tetra- hydrocannabinol (V)	209 282	33,500 2,910	10 mg/ml
11-nor-Δ^9-tetrahydro- cannabinol-9-carboxylic acid (VI)	209 275 283	54,090 2,150 2,050	10 mg/ml

of I in plasma could be detected at 273.7 nm, it seemed reasonable to anticipate a lower detection limit of 2-5 ng/ml for I using 209 nm detection. Similar reasoning seemed to be applicable to VI. For I, this degree of sensitivity would be adequate for monitoring plasma levels following marijuana smoking, cf. Figure 2.

One major obstacle to effective use of UV monitoring of HPLC effluent in the range of 200-220 nm was solvent incompatibility. Two types of incompatibilities were noted: 1) impurities in the solvent; 2) solvent functional group absorbance, i.e. UV cutoff. The former incompatibility was easily overcome by using high quality solvents from the same lot. Solvent functional group absorbance proved to be the more difficult of the two incompatibilities.

Our earlier work with a polar silica gel column had demonstrated the need for a solvent of higher dielectric constant, i.e. methylene chloride, to effectively elute the cannabinoids. Methylene chloride could not be used at 209 nm due to its UV cutoff at 230 nm. The other partner in the earlier used gradient program, heptane, was compatible with use for lower wavelength monitoring because of its 200 nm cutoff. Yet heptane by itself was not polar enough to elute the cannabinoids from the silica gel column. To accomplish elution and separation of the cannabinoids, varying percentages of isopropyl alcohol (UV cutoff of 210 nm) was added to heptane. In general, the percentages used were less than 3%. Initial resolution and retention times for I-IV were satisfactory using 3% isopropanol in heptane and isocratic conditions. However, within a few weeks of continuous analysis using these conditions, both resolution and retention times of these cannabinoids changed and became unsatisfactory for use in an assay method. Presumably this change in resolution of the silica gel column was due to hydrogen bonding of isopropyl alcohol to the active sites since removal of isopropyl alcohol from the mobile phase and continued elution with heptane over approximately two days would restore some resolution characteristics.

For the above reasons, 1,4-dioxane (UV cutoff of 220 nm) was substituted for isopropyl alcohol in the mobile phase. An isocratic system consisting of 0.4% 1,4-dioxane in heptane, flow rate of 120 ml/hr, a 10 micron silica gel column, and monitoring at 209 nm, proved to be satisfactory for separating I-IV. With this system 20 ng of I could be accurately quantitated but levels lower than that became a problem due to a poor signal to noise ratio. This poor signal to noise ratio was apparently due to the 220 nm cutoff of 1,4-

dioxane. To overcome this problem a mobile phase split-
ter was devised such that mobile phase from the pump
entered a bifurcation and was equally split into 10
micron silica gel columns. One column was connected to
a flow cell in the sample beam and the other column to
a flow cell in the reference beam of a dual beam spectrophotometer. The analyzed sample was injected onto
the column attached to the flow cell in the sample beam.
This modified detection system achieved the original
goal of reducing signal to noise ratio and permitted
detection of 2 ng of I. However, the low detection
limit was of itself not adequate since later work using
human plasma known to be free of I demonstrated an endogenous constituent of identical retention time.
Efforts to separate this endogenous constituent by mobile phase alterations (i.e. changing percentages of
1,4-dioxane), flow rate, or temperature changes proved
to be unproductive.
     As an alternate approach to separating these can-
nabinoids from endogenous plasma constituents, some
bonded phase columns operated in a normal phase mode
were investigated. Prior experience in our laboratory
(13) had demonstrated the dependability of silica gel
when used to process numerous plasma samples. That is,
resolution was unaffected by the numerous endogenous
plasma constituents continually placed on the column.
The same type of experience with bonded-phase columns
was unavailable and thus is became important to explore
plasma analyses with these types of columns. Initial
work was begun with a 10 micron alkylnitrile column.
Based upon the experience with mobile phase solvents
using a silica gel column, heptane which contained
small percentages of either isopropyl alcohol or 1,4-
dioxane was used. Eventually a mobile phase containing
0.3% isopropyl alcohol was selected as the optimum
elution mixture. This selection was based on the fact
that resolution of the individual cannabinoids was unaffected over a prolonged period of time and permitted
greater sensitivity for I. Small percentages of 1,4-
dioxane produced higher pressure requirements in addition to affecting detection sensitivity of I by virtue
of greater baseline noise.
     Although 0.3% isopropyl alcohol in heptane using
an isocratic mode on the alkylnitrile column was excellent for separating individual cannabinoids it
proved to be of little value for resolving I from one
endogenous constituent in human plasma. Figure 4 is
a typical chromatogram of human plasma which is free of
I and superimposed upon it is the chromatogram of the
same plasma to which I has been added. As noted in

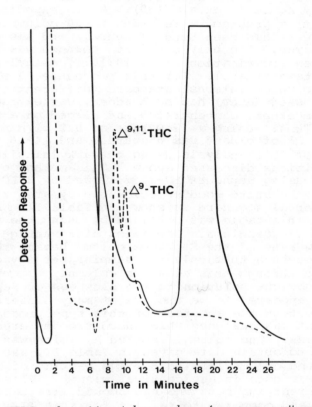

Figure 4.   HPLC analysis of (——), human plasma from a non-marijuana smoker compared to (– – –), the same plasma to which VIII ($\Delta^{9,11}$-THC) and I (Δ^9-THC) have been added.   Mobile phase of 0.3% isopropyl alcohol in heptane used on an alkylnitrile column.

this figure the endogenous constituent is small but
would obviously interfere with detection or quantification of I. Again as we experienced earlier, modification of HPLC conditions did not produce the required
resolution.

Our experience with the non-separation of I from
an endogenous plasma constituent had also been experienced by Agurell, et al. (10). As an expedient solution to this problem, a Sephadex LH-20 column clean-up
procedure as had been used by Agurell and his co-workers
was employed. The only condition changed was the eluting solvent combination used, 10:10:1, methylene chlo-
ride:heptane:ethanol. For this procedure, 1 ml of blood
plasma to which internal standard (different choices
are discussed later) had been added, was extracted with
petroleum ether, concentrated and placed on a Sephadex
LH-20 column. Using a flow rate of 0.2 ml/min. the
first 14 ml of eluant was discarded and 14-26 ml collected for HPLC analysis using the alkylnitrile column
and conditions discussed above. This method of plasma
clean-up using Sephadex LH-20 followed by HPLC analysis
proved to be quite good as evidenced by area ratio of
I to internal standard as shown in Table II. All data
shown in this table was obtained by using the same
Sephadex LH-20 column. The major disadvantage was the
slow flow rate of the Sephadex column became the limiting factor such that only two samples per day could be
processed through this clean-up column.

An obvious solution to the slowness of Sephadex
clean-up appeared to be the use of many different columns. To test the accuracy of this type procedure an
experiment was designed which used two different Sephadex columns. One column, labeled A, which was the same
one used to obtain data given in Table II, was compared
to a second column labeled B. The packing of Column
A and B was done in an identical manner. Plasma from
two different subjects who had smoked marijuana was
analyzed and compared to results for that same sample
obtained using the HPLC-MS technique (13). As shown
in Table III, plasma samples from subject T.V. were
processed through column A whereas samples from subject
R.B. were processed through column B. A standard curve
was obtained for each Sephadex column by processing
plasma from laboratory workers, known to be free of
marijuana, to which had been added 2, 5, 10, 20, and 30
ng/ml of I. The samples were alternated such that a
standard was processed followed by a subject's plasma,
etc., until all samples had been processed. A total of
4.5 days was required to process all the samples through
Sephadex columns. However, all samples were processed
by HPLC on the same day.

TABLE II

Accuracy and Precision of Sephadex-HPLC Method for Analysis of
Δ^9-*Tetrahydrocannabinol*

Concentration of Δ^9-THC (ng/ml)	Area Ratio Average (Range)	Number of Determinations	Standard Deviation
5	0.082 (0.070-0.093)	10	± 0.007
10	0.158 (0.148-0.167)	10	± 0.008
20	0.280 (0.257-0.306)	10	± 0.018
30	0.418 (0.403-0.435)	10	± 0.011
40	0.540 (0.504-0.580)	10	± 0.024
50	0.688 (0.653-0.731)	10	± 0.027

TABLE III

Sephadex-HPLC Analysis of Marijuana Smokers Plasma
Compared to HPLC-MS Analysis[a]

Subject	Sephadex Column	Post-Marijuana Smoking time (hrs.)	ng/ml Δ^9-THC Found HPLC	HPLC-MS
T.V.	A	0[b]	10.0	11.3
		0.25	25.7	34.6
		0.5	19.5	16.5
		1.0	11.7	10.1
R.B.	B	0[b]	4.1	5.7
		0.25	60.9	43.7
		0.5	92.5	18.9

[a]Method described in Reference 13
[b]Sample taken prior to marijuana smoking

As noted in Table III, results from column A are in
quite good agreement with the reference method, whereas
those obtained on column B are inconsistent at two time
intervals.   These results pointed out one of the major
problems with processing samples through different
Sephadex columns which can be attributed in part to
varability in flow rate as a function of column head
pressure.   These results indicate that a practical assay
can be achieved only if one column is used or alternately, carefully controlling flow rate changes due to
ambient pressure changes.

Not specifically covered in the previous discussion
was the search for an appropriate internal standard.
Four different compounds, hexahydrocannabinol (VII),
$\Delta^{9,11}$-tetrahydrocannabinol (VIII), dimethylheptylpyran
(IX), and cyclopentyldimethylheptylpyran (X) were all
evaluated as internal standards.   Of these compounds,
IX proved to be best for the Sephadex-HPLC method.
Even though IX has the possibility of a number of iso-
meric forms, it gave only one peak upon HPLC analysis.

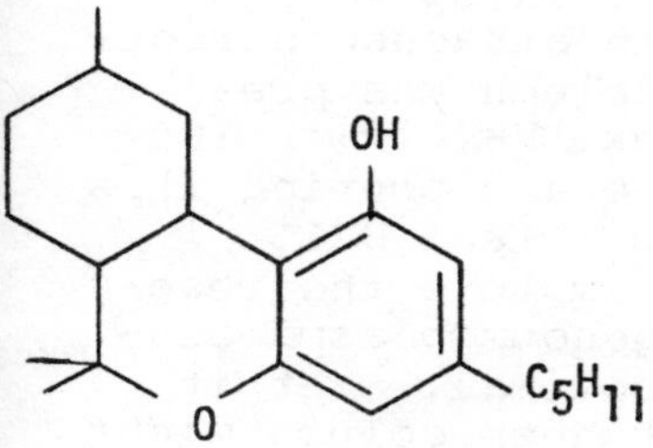

VII

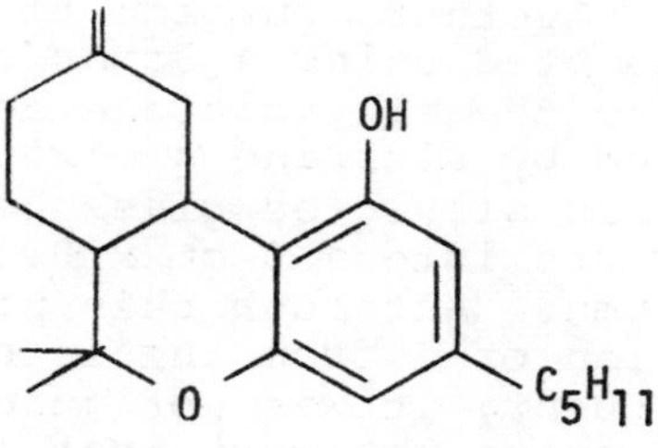

VIII

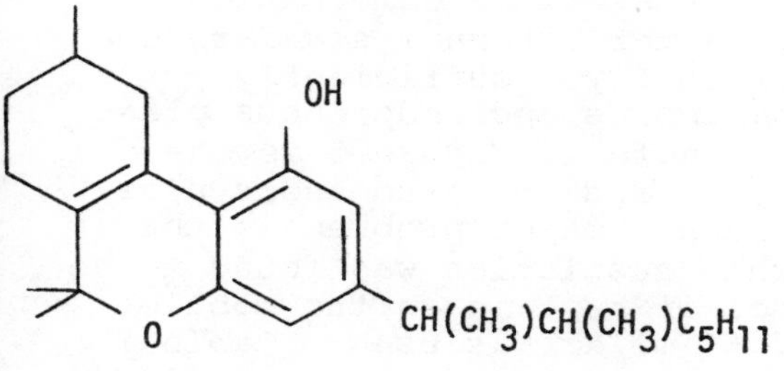

IX

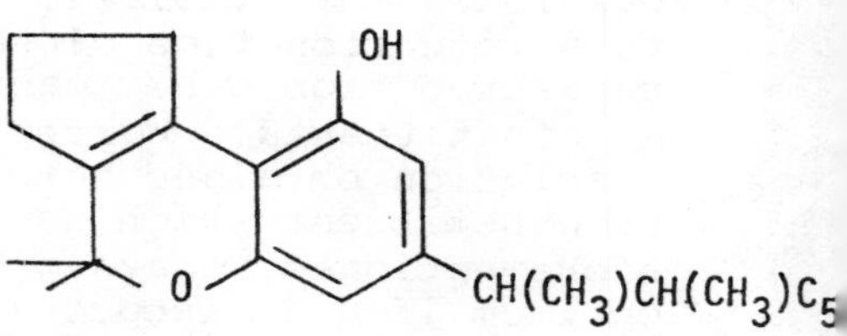

X

Partial success with Sephadex LH-20 prior clean-up of plasma prompted the examination of other techniques which might remove endogenous plasma constituents known to interfere with the HPLC assay. One such technique was to explore extracting solvents other than petroleum ether. For example, benzene, heptane, and ethyl acetate either singly or mixed with small percentages of isopropyl alcohol gave results comparable to petroleum ether alone. In addition two different protein precipitation techniques were investigated. A 1:1 ratio of methanol or 5% aqueous trichloroacetic acid when added to plasma produced a precipitate which was removed by centrifugation. The resultant supernatant fluid was adjusted to pH 7.4 and extracted with petroleum ether. With either method there was no I found in this supernate when analyzed by HPLC. Conversely, if the precipitate was resuspended in water and extracted with petroleum ether the resulting HPLC chromatogram was very similar to that obtained with a simple petroleum ether extract. This finding supported previous work (18) that I is largely protein bound.

Another approach to preparatory clean-up was attempted using a Sephadex LH-20 column attached directly to the alkylnitrile column. This column was prepared by slurring a mixture of Sephadex LH-20 with 100 micron silylated glass beads in heptane and pouring this mixture into a 5 cm x 0.15 cm stainless steel HPLC column. Although this pre-column did improve the resolution of I from the interfering endogenous plasma constituent, it was not judged as being optimal. Yet it was quite apparent that some type of tandem column might have distinct advantages. This type of reasoning led ultimately to use of tandem alkylamine-alkylnitrile columns. The order of the columns was found not to be critical even though the result shown in Figure 5 was obtained using the alkylamine column prior to the alkylnitrile column. With this column combination it was found that VIII was a better internal standard due to a retention time closer to I yet sufficiently separated from other cannabinoids and endogenous plasma constituents. Worthy of note in Figure 5 is the resolution obtained between I and the endogenous plasma constituent which had been a major problem in the aforementioned assays. This resolution was found to be optimum if 0.6% isopropanol in heptane as the mobile phase with a flow rate of 60 ml/hr was used. Table IV summarizes the different percentages of isopropanol used in the development. The overall resolution was better in this tandem column but sensitivity was not quite as good as had been observed with the alkylnitrile

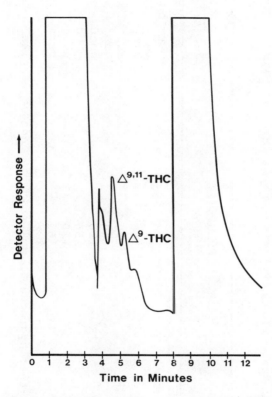

Figure 5. HPLC analysis of human plasma from a marijuana smoker to which VIII (Δ⁹,¹¹-THC) has been added as internal standard. Mobile phase of 0.6% isopropyl alcohol in heptane used on a tandem alkylamine–alkylnitrile column with a flow rate of 60 mL/hr.

TABLE IV

Determination of Isopropanol Percentage and
Flow Rates with Alkylamine-Alkylnitrile Columns

% Isopropanol in Heptane	Flow Rate ml/hr	Resolution[a]
0.1	60	very poor
0.1	120	very poor
0.2	60	fair
0.2	120	fair
0.3	60	good
0.3	120	good
0.3	150	good
0.5	120	good
0.6	60	very good

[a]Resolution of Δ^9-tetrahydrocannabinol from the endogenous plasma constituent.

column alone. Whereas the alkylnitrile column method
permitted 5 ng/ml determinations, the alkylamine-alkylnitrile method allowed only 10 ng/ml determinations.
If however, detection was the objective, 5 ng/ml limit
was practical in the tandem method. As with the other
HPLC techniques, this method was compared to the reference HPLC-MS technique. Table V gives data obtained on
plasma from a marijuana smoker using both methods. The
only notable variance between the two methods occurred
with the two hour sample which was received by our
laboratory in a broken tube.

Work at present continues in our laboratory using
this latter method. More experience is needed with the
tandem column combination prior to its replacement of
the proven HPLC-MS technique. Recent experience with
the tandem column has shown that accurate and precise
data can be obtained on freshly obtained plasma or plasma which has only been refrozen once. Upon repeated
thawing and refreezing of the sample, values of I become unreliable. Presumably this is due to appearance
of an endogenous substance with a retention time similar to I. Further work will be necessary to fully
explain this phenomenon.

REVERSE PHASE HPLC

As discussed earlier, I has two principal metabolites in plasma, viz., V and VI. Studies by Wall, et
al. (19,20) had demonstrated that nor-acid VI occurs
in somewhat larger amounts than V in human plasma but
both in smaller amounts than I. Since as was shown in
Table I, VI has a greater molar absorbivity than V at
209 nm, it was apparent that assay of VI by HPLC would
have the greatest chance for success since its absorptivity was slightly greater than I.

Initial work on the assay for this metabolite using normal phase HPLC as was developed for I was impractical due to the polar nature of VI. Using such
systems resulted in long analysis time, broad eluting
bands, as well as poor sensitivity for the polar metabolite. These findings led then to an investigation of
reverse-phase HPLC for analysis of this metabolite.
The first type of HPLC column investigated was a polymeric octadecylsilane column. A number of different
mobile phase systems were examined as shown in Table VI.
For these isocratic studies a flow rate of 40 ml/hr and
100 ng of VI in mobile phase as the analyte was used.
As noted in this data, water:acetonitrile seemed to
offer greatest promise as a potential mobile phase due
to the greater observed sensitivity. However, the

TABLE V

Comparison of HPLC-UV and HPLC-MS[a] Techniques

Time Post-dose (hrs)	ng/ml Found HPLC-MS	HPLC-MS
0.0[b]	0	0
0.0833	87	85
0.1666	57	55
0.25	42	35
0.50	27	21
0.75	19	18
1.00	17	14
1.50	15	13
2.00[c]	22	9
4.00	0	2

[a]Method described in Reference 13

[b]Sample taken prior to marijuana smoking

[c]Sample container broken in transit

short retention time placed VI on the trailing edge of endogenous substances found in plasma and made accurate quantification difficult.

The most satisfactory HPLC conditions for analysis of VI was ultimately achieved using a phenyl-bonded phase column in the reverse phase mode. Based upon the experience described above for polymeric octadecylsilane, water:acetonitrile was exclusively used as mobile phase in the development work.

To achieve adequate resolution and sensitivity for VI from endogenous blood plasma constituents, a gradient HPLC program was employed. The program starts at 60:40, water:acetonitrile for 3 minutes and then is increased to 40:60, water:acetonitrile over a 2 minute period, held at that ratio for 5 minutes, then returned to 60:40, water:acetonitrile over a 2 minute period. Using this HPLC gradient program, VI is eluted at 2.7 minutes as shown in Figure 6. As noted in this figure, VI is eluted during the isocratic portion of the HPLC program. The major purpose of the gradient program is to clear the endogenous blood plasma compounds so that the overall analysis time is reduced. Although not shown in Figure 6, V elutes at 3.4 minutes.

Once the proper HPLC conditions were achieved for VI, a study was conducted to determine which pH and extraction solvent would be optimum. For this study 100 ng of VI was added to 1 ml of plasma taken from laboratory workers known to be free of marijuana. Each plasma was run in triplicate using pH and extraction conditions shown in Table VII. As a result of these studies, a pH of 4 and benzene containing 1.5% isopropanol was used as the extracting conditions for analysis of VI since this pH gave consistently better appearing chromatograms than did pH 2.5.

The relative amount of UV recovered was determined by comparing total area of the peak with that of a 100 ng sample placed directly on the instrument. This extraction study did however, point out a potential problem with reverse phase analysis. Direct extraction of plasma with benzene-isopropanol at pH 4 followed by HPLC analysis produced increasing pressures, losses in resolution and sensitivity in a short period of time. Further work demonstrated that this effect was related to lipoidal material in plasma. A preliminary extraction with petroleum ether at ambient pH prior to acidifying and extracting with benzene-isopropanol alleviated this problem.

Once the extracting and HPLC conditions were worked out the method was evaluated in plasma of a marijuana smoker.

TABLE VI

Mobile Phase Studies Using Polymeric Octadecylsilane To
Analyze 11-Nor-Δ⁹-tetrahydrocannabinol-9-carboxylic Acid

Mobile Phase[a]	Composition	Retention Time (min)	Peak Height (in.)	Half Width
Water:acetonitrile	30:70	0.8	10	0.15
	50:50	0.9	10	0.15
	55:45	0.9	8	0.15
	60:40	0.95	7	0.15
	65:35	1.45	5	0.25
	70:30	6.0	1	3.00
Water:methanol	35:65	1.1	6.5	0.2
	40:60	1.25	5	0.25
	45:55	1.45	3.5	0.35
Water:acetonitrile: ethylene glycol	50:48:2	1.15	7	0.18
	50:45:5	1.15	7	0.18
	50:40:10	1.15	7	0.18
	55:43:2	1.25	6	0.2
	55:40:5	1.35	5.5	0.22
	60:39:1	1.7	4	0.35
	60:38:2	1.6	5	0.3
Water:acetonitrile: methanol	20:50:30	0.85	6	0.15
	45:45:10	1.15	6	0.2

TABLE VI (Con't)

Mobile Phase[a]	Composition	Retention Time (min)	Peak Height (in.)	Half Width
Water:acetonitrile: methanol	50:45:5	1.25	6	0.2
	50:30:20	1.6	4	0.3
	55:40:5	1.5	4.5	0.3
	55:35:10	1.9	2.5	0.5
	58:37:5	1.7	4	0.4
	60:38:2	1.75	4.5	0.3
	60:35:5	2.2	2.5	0.5

[a]Flow rate of 40 ml/hr and 100 ng of 11-nor-Δ^9-tetrahydrocannabinol-9-carboxylic acid analyzed.

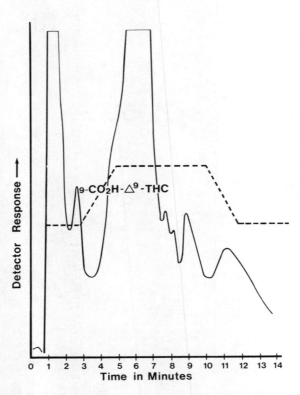

Figure 6. *HPLC analysis of human plasma from a non-marijuana smoker to which 100 ng/mL of VI has been added. A gradient (superimposed with dashed line) beginning with 60:40, water:acetonitrile was used on a phenyl-bonded phase column.*

TABLE VII

Evaluation of Extraction pH and Solvents for 11-Nor-Δ^9-tetrahydrocannabinol-9-carboxylic Acid from Plasma

pH	Extracting Solvent	Relative Amount Recovered[a]
ambient (7.4)	petroleum ether	none
2.5	petroleum ether	none
2.5	benzene (1.5% isopropanol)	70%
2.5	benzene (3% isopropanol)	60%
4	benzene (1.5% isopropanol)	70%

[a]One extraction of plasma

Table VIII gives values determined for both I and VI in
this smoker. The most apparent feature of this data is
the high levels of VI as compared to I.

TABLE VIII

Comparison of Plasma Levels of
I and VI in a Marijuana Smoker[a]

| Time (hrs) | ng/ml Found | |
	I[b]	VI
0[c]	0.4	300
0.25	57.9	1540
0.5	24.8	1840
1.0	14.8	3000
2.0	10.7	1480
3.0	2.4	2040
4.0	6.2	1900
12.0	5.8	2650
24.0	2.5	1920

[a]Marijuana cigarette contained 10.8 mg of I.

[b]Determined by HPLC-MS method.

[c]Sample taken prior to marijuana smoking.

Two explanations could be offered to explain the observed values of VI. The first is based on the observation (21) that I is largely metabolized during the
first pass through the liver. Second, is the presence
of some other substance with a retention time identical
to that of VI. The latter explanation could certainly
be plausible since acid metabolites of II and III would
be anticipated to give retention times similar to VI.
Work will continue in our laboratory in an attempt to
elucidate the correct answer.

To improve on the precision and accuracy of the
assay for VI, a search was begun to find an appropriate
internal standard. Since no synthetic analogs of VI
or other cannabinoid-like acids were available when
this work was initiated, a number of readily available
compounds which would not frequently appear in plasma
were evaluated. Most of these were selected based upon
their acid properties as is apparent in Table IX which
lists the compounds studied. As shown, most of the

more acidic phenol-type compounds were unretained using the HPLC reverse phase method. Only when more hydrocarbon characteristics were added to the phenols did retention of the compounds become more apparent, for example the biphenylphenols. When the retention time of VI, viz., 2.7 minutes, is compared to those compounds studied it is obvious that VI would be classified as an intermediate acid. This finding was used in part to select the pH 4 extracting conditions discussed earlier. Also as noted in Table IX, benzylbiphenyl was the only compound found which, based upon retention time, appeared acceptable as an internal standard. Subsequent work demonstrated that benzylbiphenyl was not completely satisfactory as an internal standard since the petroleum ether extract required to remove lipids also largely extracted benzylbiphenyl. Thus to avoid extraction of internal standard it was necessary to add benzylbiphenyl after the preliminary extraction with petroleum ether. This method was not adequate since there was no control of VI losses during the preliminary extraction.

TABLE IX

Compounds Investigated as Internal Standard for Assay of 11-Nor-Δ^9-tetrahydrocannabinol-9-carboxylic acid

Compound	Retention Time (min)	Comments
2,3-dihydroxybenzoic acid	1.2	a
2,4-dihydroxybenzoic acid	1.2	a
2,6-dihydroxybenzoic acid	1.2	a
3,4-dihydroxybenzoic acid	1.2	a
3,5-dihydroxybenzoic acid	1.2	a
4,4'-biphenol	1.2	a
catechol	1.2	a
cis-p-hydroxycinnamic acid	1.2	a
cis-m-hydroxycinnamic acid	1.2	a
cis-o-hydroxycinnamic acid	1.2	a
pyrogallol	1.2	a
resorcinol	1.2	a
syringaldehyde	1.2	a
syringic acid	1.2	a
xanthydrol	1.2	a
olivetol	1.2	a
acetohexamide	1.2	a
cinchophene	1.2	a
vanillin	1.2	a
o-vanillin	1.2	a

TABLE IX (Con't)

Compound	Retention Time (min)	Comments
mephenytoin	1.2	a
p-hydroxybenzaldehyde	1.2	a
4-hydroxycoumarin	1.2	a
7-hydroxycoumarin	1.2	a
biphenol	1.2	a
2-biphenylcarboxylic acid	1.2	a
4-biphenylcarboxylic acid	1.2	a
4-phenylphenol	1.4	b
1-naphthol	1.4	b
amobarbital	1.4	b
ethosuximide	1.4	b
phenoxybenzamine	1.4	b
4-biphenylphenol	2.9	c
2-biphenylphenylphenol	3.1	c
biphenyl	4.0	d
4-(p-biphenyl)-2-methylthiazole	5.0	b
benzylbiphenyl	11.0	e

[a]unretained; [b]not resolved from an endogenous plasma peak; [c]not resolved from VI; [d]not water soluble, [e]resolved from endogenous plasma peaks.

SIMULTANEOUS ASSAY OF I AND VI

Results from the reverse phase HPLC study suggested that since a preliminary extraction of plasma with petroleum ether was required to remove lipids, that a 1 ml sample of plasma could be extracted first at a neutral pH to remove I followed by acidification to pH 4 and extraction to remove VI. Indeed this was found to be practical. Thus to 1 ml of plasma could be added either d_3-I or VIII, depending upon which assay method was to be used, as internal standard followed by extraction with petroleum ether. To the plasma would then be added 1 ml of pH 4 buffer and benzylbiphenyl followed by extraction with benzene-isopropanol.

An attractive alternative to the above procedure would have been one extraction to remove both I and VI followed by HPLC analysis. As a prelude to this study it was found that the reverse phase HPLC conditions with slight modifications in the gradient program was capable of assay for both VI and I which had retention times of

2.7 and 8.5 minutes, respectively. Thus simultaneous HPLC assay of I and VI seemed practical by reverse phase. However, the major problem encountered was simultaneous extraction of both compounds. As pointed out earlier, if lipiodal material was placed upon the reverse phase column, serious pressure and resolution problems resulted. Therefore petroleum ether was eliminated as a possible extracting solvent based on its ability to extract lipids. Similarly eliminated were other extracting solvents such as ethyl ether and chloroform. Benzene-isopropanol, as pointed out earlier also tends to remove lipids. A number of other solvents were tried but they either removed lipids or did not extract I and VI very efficiently. Thus this rather grandiose plan for simultaneous analysis of I and VI proved to be impractical due to lack of an effective matrix separation technique.

CONCLUSIONS

Both normal phase and reverse phase HPLC methods were studied as analytical techniques for analysis of I and VI in human plasma. Normal phase was found to be more satisfactory for separation of I from plasma constituents whereas reverse phase was the choice for VI. Although reverse phase HPLC could be used to simultaneously assay for both I and VI when placed directly on the instrument, it was not practical for analysis of plasma extracts.

Detection of either I or VI in HPLC eluent was found to be practical using UV light at 209 nm. Mobile phases used had to be compatible with monitoring at this wavelength to obtain the sensitivity needed for plasma assays. In the assay for I a 0.3% isopropanol in heptane solution as mobile phase met these criteria as did water:acetonitrile in the assay for VI. The assay developed for I required the use of two tandem bonded-phase columns to adequately separate drug and endogenous plasma constituents.

Both assay methods show promise as primary detection and determination methods of marijuana use. The assay for I using UV detection appears adequate if plasma has not been thawed and refrozen. If refreezing has occurred, it becomes necessary to use HPLC/MS which is not affected by this phenomenon. The assay for VI needs to be standardized against the HPLC/MS technique. Only recently did d-VI become available and will be utilized for this new assay development.

ACKNOWLEDGEMENTS

Work reported in this article was financially supported by the U.S. Department of Transportation - National Highway Traffic Safety Administration, National Institute on Drug Abuse, and Faculty Research Funds - University of Missouri. The authors are grateful to the University of Missouri-Kansas City, School of Medicine for providing laboratory facilities for this work.

REFERENCES

(1)   Present address: Department of Pharmacology, School of Medicine, Oral Roberts University, Tulsa, Oklahoma   74171.

(2)   Edery, H. Y., Grunfeld, F., Ben-Zvi, F., and Mechoulam, R., Ann. *N.Y. Acad. Sci. 191*, 40 (1971).

(3)   Galanter, M., Wyatt, R. J., Lemberger, L., Weingartner, H., Vaughn, T. B., and Roth, W. T., *Science 176*, 934   (1972).

(4)   Doorenbos, N. J., Fetterman, P. S., Quimby, M. W., and Turner, C. E., Ann. *N.Y. Acad. Sci. 191*, 3 (1971).

(5)   Binder, M. S., Agurell, S., Leander, K., and Lindgren, J. E., *Helv. Chim. Acta 57*, 1626 (1974).

(6)   Wall, M. E., Brine, D. R., Pitt, C. G., and Perez-Reyes, M., *J. Am. Chem. Soc. 94*, 8579 (1972).

(7)   Lemberger, L., Silberstein, S., Axelrod, J., and Kopin, I., *Science 170*, 1320   (1970).

(8)   Lemberger, L., Tamarkin, N. R., Axelrod, J. and Kopin, I. J., *Science 173*, 72   (1971).

(9)   Kephalas, T. A., Kiburis, J., Michael, C. M., Miras, C. J., and Papadakis, D. P., "Marijuana: Chemistry, Biochemistry and Cellular Effects", G. G. Nahas, Ed., Springer-Verlag, New York, 1976.

(10)   Rosenfeld, J. J., Bavins, B., Roberts, J., Perkins, J., and MacPherson, A. S., *Anal. Chem. 46*, 2232   (1974).

(11)   Teale, J. D., King, L. J., Forman, E. J., and Marks, V., *Lancet 2*, 553   (1974).

(12)   Valentine, J. L., Bryant, P. J., Gutshall, P. L., Gan, O. H. M., Lovegreen, P. D., Thompson, E. D., and Niu, H. C., *J. Pharm. Sci. 66*, 1263   (1977).

(13)   Valentine, J. L., Bryant, P. J., Gutshall, P. L., Gan, O. H. M., and Driscoll, P., *Trace Substances in Environmental Health IX*, 291   (1975).

(14) Gaoni, Y. and Mechoulam, R., *J. Am. Chem. Soc. 86,* 1646 (1964).
(15) Korte, F. and Sieper, H., *Liebigs Ann. Chem. 630,* 71 (1960).
(16) Gaoni, Y. and Mechoulam, R., *Chem. Commun. 1966,* 20.
(17) Garrett, E. R. and Hunt, C. A., *J. Pharm. Sci. 62,* 1211 (1973).
(18) Wall, M. E. and Brine, D. R., "Pharmacology of Marijuana", M. Braude and S. Szara, Eds., Raven Press, New York, 1976.
(19) Wall, M. E., Harvey, T. M., Bursey, J. T., Brine, D. R., and Rosenthal, D., "Cannabinoid Assays in Humans", NIDA Research Monograph No. 7, Rockville, Maryland, 1976.
(20) Garrett, E. R. and Hunt, C. A., *J. Pharm. Sci. 66,* 395 (1977).

RECEIVED January 2, 1979.

Detection and Quantitation of Δ^9-Tetrahydrocannabinol in Plasma by Dansylation and Double Labeling

J. M. SCHERRMANN and R. BOURDON

U. E. R. de Biologie Humaine et Experimentale, Laboratoire de Biochimie, Hopital Fernand Widal, Paris V, France

H. HOELLINGER, NGUYEN-HOANG-NAM, and E. FOURNIER

I.N.S.E.R.M. Unite de Recherche de Toxicologie Experimentale, Hopital Fernand Widal, 200, Rue du Faubourg Saint Denis, 75475 Paris Cedex 10, France

Δ^9-THC is the major psychoactive constituent of Cannabis. Its detection and quantitation pose a difficult analytical problem because of its low concentration in biological fluids. Much work has been done on the identification and quantitation of Δ^9-THC, its metabolites and cannabinoids by standard methods such as radio-immunoassay (1,2), gas chromatography, either alone (3-6) or coupled with mass spectrometry (7,8) and fluorometry (9-15). All these methods endeavor to satisfy two major criteria: specificity and sensitivity.

Although radio-immunoassays are rapid and convenient to analyze large numbers of samples, they lack absolute sensitivity and specificity, since cannabinoids cross-react within a given assay. Gas chromatography is no more satisfactory. However, when combined with mass spectrometry it is far more specific and sensitive, although extremely costly. Finally, fluorometric techniques have proved suitable for many applications such as the one based on gallium chelate formation which can only be used for urine (9), and more especially for applications based on cannabinoid dansylation (16-18). However, these last techniques only allow qualitative determination of Δ^9-THC.

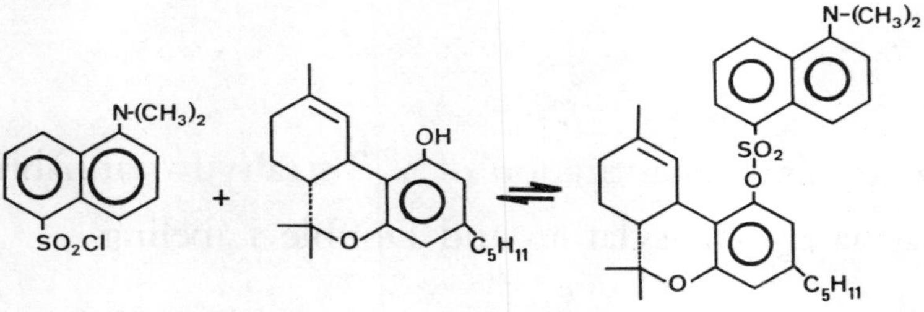

Figure 1.   Chemical derivatization of Δ^9-THC

The method we have developed for the detection and quantitation of Δ^9-THC in plasma also utilizes dansyl technology, but our methodology is based on the use of ^{14}C DANS-Cl and, for quantitative determination, on the use of $^3H_2$ Δ^9-THC as an internal standard (19-22).

PRINCIPLES OF THE METHOD

The main steps for detection are 1) Extraction of Δ^9-THC from plasma; 2) Esterification by ^{14}C DANS-Cl; 3) Purification by TLC; 4) Elution of the ^{14}C DANS-Δ^9-THC spot and measurement of ^{14}C activity.

In order to perform quantitation, the four steps listed above are preceeded by the addition of $^3H_2\Delta^9$-THC to the plasma. This is achieved in order to allow accurate determination of the quantity of Δ^9-THC initially present, by correcting the non negligible losses observed during extraction, esterification and purification as shown schematically in Figure 2.

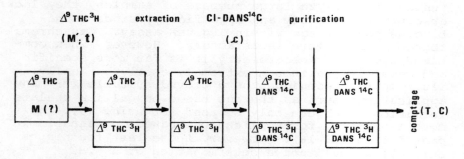

Figure 2.   Principles of the method of detecting and quantitating Δ^9-THC

The initial amount M of Δ^9-THC is given by the formula:

$$M = M' \times \frac{t}{c} \times \frac{C}{T}$$

where M' = amount of $^3H_2\Delta^9$-THC added
    t = specific activity (SA) of $^3H_2\Delta^9$-THC
    c = specific activity (SA) of ^{14}C DANS-Cl
    C = ^{14}C activity measured at the end of analysis
        (dpm)
    T = ^3H activity at the end of analysis (dpm).

The known parameters are: M', c and t.
Measurement of M is obtained by the determination of T
and C in the fraction of the product isolated at the
end of the test.

PROCEDURE

A. Extraction

    1. Detection
    Four ml plasma are extracted twice with 4 ml of
the following solvent: methyl acetate/petroleum ether/
ethanol (66:33:1.5 v/v). After centrifugation, the
organic extracts are evaporated to dryness, dissolved
into 4 ml hexane and again extracted twice with 2 ml
Claisen's alkali reagent. The alkaline solutions are
acidified with 1 ml N HCl (pH = 1.5) and then extracted
twice with 4 ml hexane. This last solution is evaporated to dryness and the residue dissolved in the
necessary amount of acetone and then transferred into
a hemolysis tube.
    2. Quantitation
    The above steps are preceded by the addition of
50 µl $^3H_2\Delta^9$-THC to 4 ml plasma and by one hour's incubation at 37°C.

B. Esterification, purification and counting

    In a hemolysis tube, 60 nmoles ^{14}C DANS-Cl solu-
tion in 60 µl acetone, and 15 µl 0.5 M Na_2CO_3 buffer
are added either to 50 µl of the acetone solution (extraction) or to a solution of 3.18 nmoles Δ^9-THC
(yield study). Simultaneously with each test, a blank
is made up under the same conditions, but without Δ^9-
THC. The tubes are stoppered, wrapped in aluminum
foil and incubated for one hour at 40°C. After cool-
ing, 18 nmoles of unlabeled DANS Δ^9-THC (carrier),
100 µl N NaOH and 500 µl distilled water are added to
the preparation. The solution is then stirred and

extracted twice with 1 ml ethyl acetate. The organic
phases are joined together then evaporated to dryness
and dissolved in 200 µl ethyl acetate. Then 20 µl of
this solution are spotted on a Merck 60 F 254 silanized
silica gel plate and developed with the solvent system
cyclohexane - ethyl acetate (95:5). The DANS-Δ^9-THC
spot is detected with UV, scraped and eluted into a
counting vial containing 10 ml scintillation liquid.
Activities are expressed in dpm after correction for
quenching of the activity of each sample from the background due to the blank.

RESULTS

A. Extraction (See Table I)

     After studying ^{14}CΔ^9-THC extraction using five
solvent systems, each with a different composition and
nature, we chose the following system: methyl acetate/
petroleum ether/ethanol (66:33:1.5 v/v) which gives
93% yield after two extractions. As the organic extract is rich in lipids, we then proceeded to a purification based on selective extraction of phenols by
modified Claisen's alkali reagent, which gives 70%
yield (8). Note: the same treatment using aqueous
sodium or potassium hydroxide solutions does not produce identical results.

B. Esterification

     Dansylation of amines and phenols is a classical
reaction. However when applied to Δ^9-THC, it calls
for special conditions, first on account of the use
^{14}C DANS-Cl and second because of the influence of
various physico-chemical parameters.

     1. Temperature and reaction time.
     The maximum yield of ^{14}C DANS-Δ^9-THC (22.5 ± 0.6%)
is obtained in 120 minutes, but as early as the fif-
teenth minute the rate of esterification is considerably slowed. A comparative study conducted for 24 hours
at room temperature did not show how the yield could
be significantly increased. The reaction time does not
therefore have much effect on the dansylation yield.
Consequently, it is preferable to operate at maximum
temperature for a brief period, i.e. for one hour at
40-45°C.

TABLE 1

Extraction Study of Δ^9-THC from Plasma

Solvents	Volume of solvents/ plasma	Number of Extractions	Yield of Concentration %
Hexane	98.5	4	80
Isoamyl alcohol	1.5		
Heptane	98.5	3	80
Ethanol	1.5		
Ethanol	2/1	2	83
Methyl acetate	67	1	85
Petroleum ether	33	3	90
Methyl acetate	66	1	87
Petroleum ether (40-60°C)	33		
Ethanol	1.5	2	93

2. pH, nature, volume and molarity of the buf-
    fer (Fig. 3, Tables II and III).
DANS-Δ^9-THC synthesis at preparative scale does
not require a buffered medium. On the other hand, the
esterification yield at the nanomole level not only
varies with the pH but according to the nature of the
buffer. The different pH ranges tested showed that
maximum esterification is obtained for 10.6 pH 12.3
with an 0.5<M<Na_2CO_3 solution.

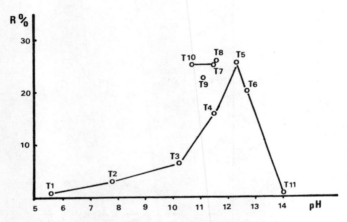

*Figure 3. Influence of pH and the nature of the buffer on the yield (R): (T1),
H_2O, pH 5.5; (T2), KH_2PO_4/Na_2HPO_4, pH 7.7; (T3), $Na_2HPO_4/NaOH$, pH 10.2;
(T4), $H_3BO_3/KCl/NaOH$, pH 11.5; (T5), $H_3BO_3/KCl/NaOH$, pH 12.3; (T6),
$H_3BO_3/KCl/NaOH$, pH 12.7; (T7), Na_2CO_3, 1 M, pH 11.5; (T8), Na_2CO_3, 5 M,
pH 11.6; (T9), Na_2CO_3, 1 M, pH 11.1; (T10), Na_2CO_3, 3 M, pH 10.6; (T11), Claisen's alkali, pH 14.*

3. ^{14}C DANS-Cl excess (Fig. 4)
    Experience has shown that ^{14}C DANS-Cl excess is
a predominant factor in esterification. Whereas at
preparative scale five times more DANS-Cl (in moles)
are sufficient to obtain a DANS Δ^9-THC yield of about
60%, this does not suffice to obtain an acceptable
yield in the case of microsynthesis. A study of the
effects of ^{14}C DANS-Cl excess in relation to Δ^9-THC
(r = ^{14}C DANS/Cl/Δ^9-THC) shows that the yield varies
in three ways:
- for 5< r <30, increasing the amount of ^{14}C DANS-Cl
  gradually displaces the reaction towards the ester,
- for 30< r <300, the yield becomes stable at around
  20%,

- beyond this (r > 300) the yield increases as a function of the ^{14}C DANS-Cl excess and catches up with the values observed at preparative scale in (Fig. 4).

TABLE II

Influence of the Volume of the Buffer and the % H_2O on the Yield (R).

Buffer		R%
μl	%	
0	0	1.1
25	5	14.7
50	10	25.3
60	12	26.8
70	14	22.7
80	16	19.5
90	18	15.3
100	20	14.3
200	40	12.8

TABLE III

Influence of the Molarity of the Na_2CO_3 Buffer on the Yield (R).

μM	pH	R%
0.1	5.5	0.9
1	8.1	1.8
2.5	11.5	25.3
5	11.5	25.0
25	11.6	25.3
50	11.1	22.5
100	11.1	23.8
150	10.6	25.0

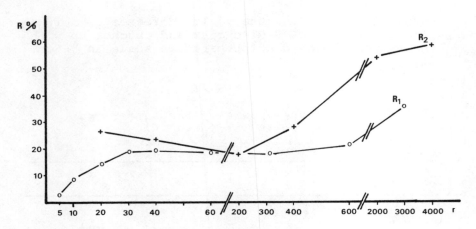

Figure 4. Influence of the excess of ^{14}C DANS-Cl on the yield (R). (R_1), reaction volume of 500 μL; (R_2), reaction volume of 125 μL. ($r = \ ^{14}$-DANS-Cl/Δ^9-THC)

The variation of the yield as a function of r does not therefore give a linear response except in the plateau zone. It is therefore impossible to refer to a standard curve, plotted independently. This makes it necessary to use an internal standard allowing correction of the effects of non linearity, since this standard's behavior is a satisfactory reflection of the behavior of Δ^9-THC in the test sample.

In order to check the identical nature of both behaviors, i.e. the absence of isotopic effects, yields were estimated for two amounts of Δ^9-THC (500 and 5 ng) corresponding to two distinct zones of the standard curve (r = 40 and r = 4000 respectively), with the same quantity (1 ng) of $^3H_2\Delta^9$-THC. The values obtained show that $^3H_2\Delta^9$-THC incorporated does not modify the R variations already described, since the yield is 17.5% in the first case and 49.5% in the second. In addition, it should be noted that although the amount of 1 ng $^3H_2\Delta^9$-THC can be ignored in relation to 500ng, the same does not apply to the lower limit of sensitivity for which the result must take into account the presence of the tritiated addition.

The yield therefore depends very much on the ^{14}C DANS-Cl excess, since a large excess of labeled reagent cannot be used. On the other hand, the lower the Δ^9-THC concentration, the higher the ester yield, which is conductive to satisfactory detection sensitivity.

The influence of the concentration of the reagents was checked under the optimal conditions described above, by varying the reaction volume but keeping the amounts of Δ^9-THC and ^{14}C DANS-Cl constant. It seems that the more concentrated the reagents the higher the yield. A compromise must therefore be found between the maximum yield and the volumes of solvent which can be handled under the most favorable conditions for accuracy and reproducibility. For this purpose, it was established that the final volume can be reacted to 125 μl. (Fig. 5).

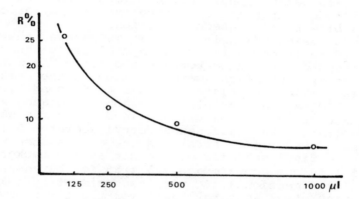

Figure 5. Yield (R) as a function of reaction volume

C. Hydrolysis and Extraction

The aim of hydrolysis is to destroy ^{14}C DANS-Cl excess which has not reacted by turning it into a salt which, under our chromatographic conditions, remains at the origin and therefore does not contaminate the ^{14}C DANS Δ^9-THC spot. TLC performed on a synthetic extract before and after hydrolysis shows that:
1) in the first case, 58% of the reagent is recovered in the chromatographic spot of ^{14}C DANS-Cl, whereas in the second there is only about 1% of the ^{14}C DANS-Cl left,
2) contamination of the ^{14}C DANS-Δ^9THC spot by carrying over is 2.7% for the non-hydrolyzed reaction and 0.02% for the hydrolyzed reaction. Unlike the technique used by KAUL (23) for chlorpromazine, hydrolysis of ^{14}C DANS-Cl excess is indispensable in this case in order to avoid high background counting. This step is followed by ^{14}C DANS-Δ^9-THC extraction. Study of the yield of this opera-

tion shows it to be quantitative (97-98%) after
two extractions with ethyl acetate.

D. Purification

TLC was carried out on various types of plates:
silica gel, silanized silica gel, cellulose and alu-
mina, as well as in several different solvent systems:
benzene, chloroform, cyclohexane, benzene/acetone
(90:10), cyclohexane/ethyl acetate (95:5), cyclo-
hexane/acetone/triethylamine (70:25:5), hexane/benzene
(60:40) and hexane/ether (80:20). Spots were either
visualized by ultraviolet or developed by pulverization
of a 1% blue B salt aqueous solution.

Tests using unlabeled DANS-Δ^9-THC showed that the
main difficulty encountered was hydrolysis of the ester-
phenol bond on the chromatographic plate. The most
satisfactory separations were obtained in the dark on
silanized silica gel plates. Under these conditions,
DANS Δ^9-THC remained stable throughout chromatography.
The best separation was obtained using the hexane/
benzene (60:40) and cyclohexane/ethyl acetate (95:5)
systems. However the latter was the only system which
produced a final satisfactory result as its background
was 225 ± 30 cpm compared to 705 ± 53 for hexane/ben-
zene. Two-dimensional TLC with two solvent systems -
cyclohexane/ethyl acetate (95:5) for the first migration followed by hexane/benzene (60:40) for the second
did not greatly improve the background, which was 291
± 34 cpm for the first development and 241 ± 31 cpm
for the second.

DISCUSSION

The usual quality criteria - detection sensitivity, linearity and reproducibility between the assays-
were determined starting with pure Δ^9-THC solutions.
Specificity is determined by means of pure solutions
of Δ^9-THC, CBN, CBD, 11-OH-Δ^9-THC and 11-OH-Δ^9-THC.
The average results of 4 determinations are given for
1000, 500, 50, 25, 10, 5, 2.5 and 1 ng of Δ^9-THC per
test tube. They are expressed both in terms of ^{14}C
activity (dpm) and of yield R% (Table IV).

A. Sensitivity

The values given in Table IV show the detection
threshold to be about 2.5 ng or 8 pmoles/tube. The
activity corresponding to 1 ng is not significantly
different from the background. For a probability of P

= 0.997 or 3 times S.D., its lower threshold is below the upper limit of the background for the same probability. For 2.5 ng on the other hand, extreme values are significantly different.

TABLE IV.

Yield of Reaction as a Function of Amount of Δ^9-THC.

Δ^9-THC ng/tube	Activity - Background Count[a] (dpm ± 1 S.D.[b]*)	R% ± 1 S.D.[b]*
1	60 ± 16	statistically insignificant
2.5	128 ± 23	77.5 ± 6.9
5	197 ± 15	59.8 ± 4.4
10	265 ± 15	40.3 ± 2.5
25	705 ± 32	42.7 ± 1.9
50	607 ± 30	18.4 ± 0.9
100	1282 ± 179	19.4 ± 2.7
500	4865 ± 761	14.8 ± 2.3
1000	13321 ± 666	20.2 ± 1.2

[a]Background count = 302 ± 18 dpm
[b]1 S.D. = one standard deviation from the mean

B. Specificity

The separation between the different dansyl-cannabinoids can be obtained by the use of the one or two-dimensional TLC. Autoradiographies showed that the major difficulty is to have a good separation between dansyl-cannabinoids and ^{14}C dansyl breakdown products which show several spots which are formed under the experimental conditions. All cannabinoids tested show one spot except CBD which give two spots. ^{14}C DANS-neutral cannabinoids give a satisfactory separation in a one-dimensional TLC using the cyclohexane/ethyl acetate (95:5) (Fig. 9) and also in a two-dimensional TLC with cyclohexane/ethyl acetate (95:5) for the first migration followed by hexane/benzene (60:40) for the second (Fig. 10). The best separation for the ^{14}C DANS-11-OH-Δ^8 and Δ^9-THC was obtained using the cyclohexane/acetone triethylamine (70:25:5) system (Fig. 11).

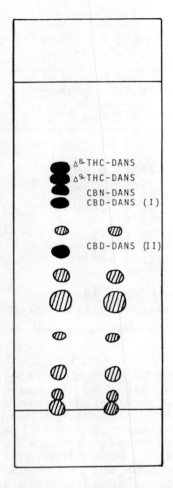

Figure 6.   Separation of neutral dansyl cannabinoids by one-dimensional TLC. Developing solvent: cyclohexane/ethyl acetate (95:5). The striped spots indicate breakdown products of DANS-Cl. The left side of the plate shows the products of derivatization of standards. The right side shows a blank reaction mixture.

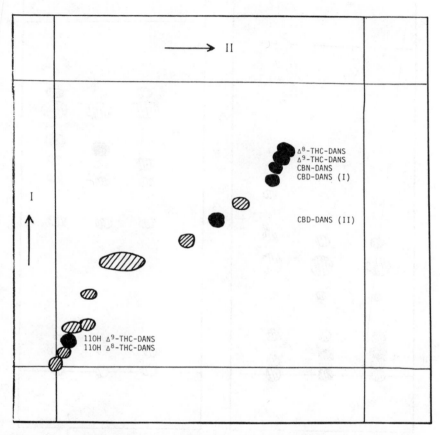

Figure 7. Separation of dansyl cannabinoids by two-dimensional TLC. Developing solvents: (I) cyclohexane/ethyl acetate (95:5); (II) hexane/benzene (60:40). The striped spots indicate breakdown products of DANS-Cl.

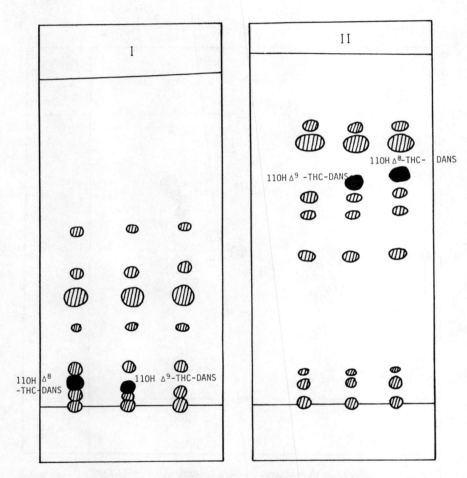

Figure 8. Separation of DANSYL-11-OH-Δ⁹-THC and Δ⁸-THC by one-dimensional TLC. Developing solvents: (I) cyclohexane/ethyl acetate (95:5); (II) cyclohexane/acetone/triethylamine (70:25:5). The striped spots indicate breakdown products of DANS-Cl. The extreme right side of I and left side of II are blank reaction mixtures.

We have never observed a positive reaction with other drugs, including drugs of abuse.

C. Linearity

The result given in Table IX confirm the observations made when the effects of ^{14}C DANS-Cl excess were studied, i.e. that the proportionality between the amount of Δ^9-THC and the response was only verified between 1000 and 50 ng.

D. Reproductibility between tests

Reproductibility between tests expresses the dispersion of the values in relation to the mean value obtained from n measurements during repetition of a given determination under identical operating conditions but with different reagents and for measurements at different stages. In the case of n = 7 determinations of 1000 of Δ^9-THC, calculation of the average yield R gave 23.6 ± 2.4%. The variation coefficient of the reproducibility index was 10.2%.

APPLICATION TO PLASMA AND URINE

The first runs of detection and quantitation of Δ^9-THC in plasma give a sensitivity in a range of 5-10 ng/ml. The activity corresponding to 10 ng/ml is very significantly different from the background. For two concentrations of 100 and 20 ng/ml we have obtained 74.8 and 18.7 ng/ml respectively.
We are now developing this technique for urine using the metabolism of cannabinoids for a very specific detection of polar cannabinoids.

CONCLUSIONS

A satisfactory solution was found for extraction giving a yield of about 70%. Among the factors affecting esterification, pH and ^{14}C DANS-Cl excess are the most important. The reaction pH must come within a range ensuring maximum ^{14}C DANS-Cl ionization. Variation in the yield as a function of ^{14}C DANS-Cl excess causes a non-linear response since the yield R can vary from 20 to 70%. Finally, during the third stage, TLC purification conditions ensure adequate separation of the reaction products and allow counting of the ^{14}C DANS-Δ^9-THC activity itself since they do not modify the structure of the ester formed. The variations in yield observed during these first two stages justify the use of $^3H_2\Delta^9$-THC as internal standard since its behavior is identical to that of non-labeled Δ^9-THC. The results of the study of these main quality criteria show the method is sensitive to about (2.5 ng) and that reproducibility of ± 10% is satisfactory.

When applied to biological fluids, the method:
1) is sensitive enough to detect a few ng/ml in plasma
2) is sufficiently accurate with the double labeling
3) has satisfactory specificity resulting from the system of purification by one or two-dimensional TLC and allows detection of polar metabolites of Δ^9-THC.

ACKNOWLEDGEMENTS

This work was supported by contract C.R.C. 76.5.067.3 from the Institut National de la Sante et de la Recherche medicale (INSERM).

REFERENCES

(1) Gross, S. T., Soares, J. R., Wong, S. L. R., and Schuster, R. E., *Nature 252*, 581 (1974).
(2) Teale, J. D., Forman, E. J., King, L. J., and Marks, V., *Lancet 2*, 553 (1974).
(3) Fenimore, D. C., Freeman, R. R. and Loy, P. R., *Anal. Chem. 45*, 2331 (1973).
(4) Garrett, E. R. and Hunt, C. A., *J. Pharm. Sci. 62*, 1211 (1973).
(5) McCallum, N. K., *J. Chromatogr. Sci. 11*, 509 (1973).
(6) Schou, J., Steentoft, A., Worm, K., Morkhadlt-Andersen, J., and Nielsen, E., *Acta. Pharmacol. 30*, 480 (1971).
(7) Agurell, S., Gustafsson, B., Holmstedt, B., Leander, K., Lindgren, J. E., Nilsson, I., Sandber, F., and Asberg, M., *J. Pharm. Pharmac. 25*, 554 (1973).
(8) Rosenfeld, J. J., Bowins, B., Roberts, J., Perkins, J., and McPherson, A. S., *Anal. Chem. 46*, 2232 (1974).
(9) Bourdon, R., *Eur. J. Toxicol. 9*, 11 (1976).
(10) Dionissiou-Asteriou, A. and Miras, C. J., *J. Pharm. Pharmac. 27*, 135 (1975).
(11) Forrest, I. S., Green D. E., Rose, S. D., Skinner, G. C., and Torres, D. M., *Res. Commun. Chem. Pathol. Pharmacol. 2*, 787 (1971).

(12) Friedrich-Fiechtl, J., Spiteller, G., Just, W. W., Werner, G., and Wiechmann, M., *Naturwissenschaften 4*, 207 (1973).

(13) Green, D. E., Rose, S. D., and Forrest, I. S., *Proc. West. Pharmacol. Sci. 14*, 187 (1971).

(14) Just, W. W., Werner, G. and Wiechmann, M., *Naturwissenschaften 59*, 222 (1972).

(15) Just, W. W., Filipovic, N., and Werner, G., *J. Chromatogr. 96*, 189 (1974).

(16) Frei-Hausler, M. and Frei, R. W., *J. Chromatogr. 79*, 209 (1973).

(17) Frei-Hausler, M. and Frei, R. W., *J. Chromatogr. 84*, 214 (1973).

(18) Melikian, I. P. and Forrest, I. S., *J. Pharm. Sci. 62*, 1025 (1973).

(19) Hardouin, J. C., *Bull. Inf. Sci. Tech. C.E.A. 147*, 45 (1970).

(20) Hoellinger, H., Nguyen-Hoang-Nam, Decauchereux, J. F., and Pichat, L. J. of *Label. Comp. Radiopharm. (in press)*.

(21) Joseph, M. H. and Halliday, J., *Anal. Biochem. 64*, 389 (1975).

(22) Maier-Hoeser, H., *Bull. Inf. Sci. Tech. C.E.A. 147*, 37 (1970).

(23) Kaul, P. N., Conway, M. W., Clark, M. L., and Huffine, J., *J. Pharm. Sci. 59*, 1745 (1970).

RECEIVED January 2, 1979.

INDEX

INDEX